CALCULATING PULLEY SPEEDS
RPM CALCULATIONS

$$\frac{\text{SPEED DRIVE PULLY} \times \text{DIA DRIVE PULLY}}{\text{DIAMETER OF DRIVEN PULLY}}$$

(CUTTERS SPEED)
(SPEED LINEAR FPS)   ~~(AIR SPEED)~~ TIP SPEED

$$\left[(\text{RPM} \div 60) \times (\text{BIT DIA} \div 12) \right] \times 3.14$$

ROCKWELL

$$\frac{3450 \times 7\frac{1}{4}\,(8)}{2\frac{1}{4}\,(3)} = 1117$$

APRX 19000 RPM ✓

SPINDLE SPEED × SPINDL PULLY SIZE =
MOTOR SPEED × MOTOR PULLY SIZE

$$\frac{3450 \times 7.25}{3.25} = X$$

DELTA   1-800-223-7278
ROCKWELL
MDL# 43-350
S#1V9617   ROCKWELL INTERNATIONAL

CALCULATING BELTS

A = DIA PULLY × 1.57

B = DIA PULLY × 1.57

C = 2× DISTANCE A TO B
SHAFT CENTERS

A + B + C = BELT LENGTH

Getting the most out of your Shaper

LOCK EDGE CUTTERS
SHOULD RUN @ 4000 RPM
NOT 7-10,000

Getting the most

out of your

Shaper

A complete manual covering all phases of shaper operations in the home workshop with over 250 photographic illustrations and line drawings.

Reprinted by
Linden Publishing Co.
3845 N. Blackstone
Fresno Calif 93726

ISBN 0-941936-01-5

89

Foreword

Getting The Most Out of Your Shaper is published as a service to power tool users. Different sizes, models, and makes of machines vary in their performance, features and ease of operation—and the editors have endeavored to make the information in this manual as general as possible.

Shapers are available in a number of sizes and designs. Selecting the proper machine for your requirements depends upon the ultimate use you will make of it. For example, you should carefully investigate the capacity of the machine to make sure that it will meet your requirements. The amount of use you intend to put your shaper to is also very important. If your machine will be used for long, sustained periods of time in the home workshop or for production work in woodworking operations, you should be sure to insist on a sturdy machine designed for large capacities. On the other hand, if your budget is limited and your use will be very intermittent, it may be well to consider a lower cost, smaller capacity machine.

For your convenience and guidance, the editors have prepared a list of "things to look for" when you buy a shaper. This list may be found on page 104 of this manual.

Originally published in 1936, this manual has been reprinted many times and has been kept up to date by addition of the latest woodworking techniques and suggestions. It is the earnest hope of the editors that it will help you "get the most out of your shaper."

SAFETY

This book is a reprint of an earlier work on the shaper and although it is one of the best books available for illustrating shaper operations and cutter combinations with their production results, it does not address safety. The operator must be familiar with standard workshop safety before using any power tool. We recommend eye and ear protection as well as a review of how fatigue affects safety. Remember, the shaper is a dangerous tool that will perform many operations for you but it can't think for you.

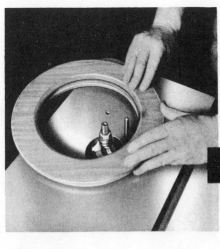

Contents

Getting the most out of your Shaper

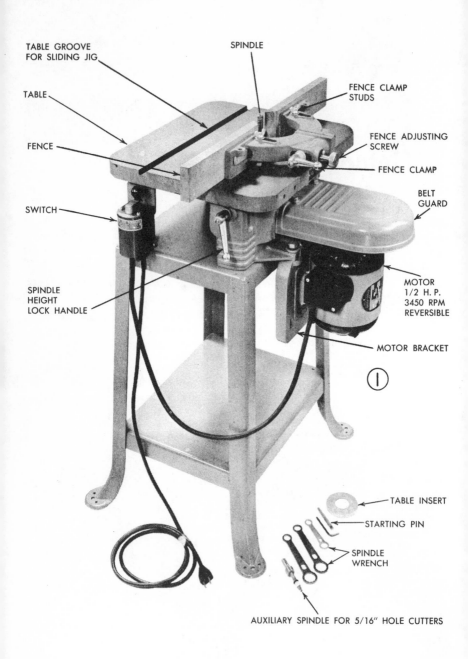

TABLE GROOVE
FOR SLIDING JIG

SPINDLE

FENCE CLAMP
STUDS

TABLE

FENCE ADJUSTING
SCREW

FENCE

FENCE CLAMP

BELT
GUARD

SWITCH

SPINDLE
HEIGHT
LOCK HANDLE

MOTOR
1/2 H. P.
3450 RPM
REVERSIBLE

MOTOR BRACKET

TABLE INSERT

STARTING PIN

SPINDLE
WRENCH

AUXILIARY SPINDLE FOR 5/16" HOLE CUTTERS

Fig. 1. Shaper Unit on steel stand.

CHAPTER ONE

The Shaper and its Adjustments

The Shaper. The shaper is a vertical spindle, differing from the drill press in that it is built primarily to withstand side thrust. The spindle is generally hollow so that auxiliary spindles can be fitted to it, much the same as drills are fitted in a drill chuck. An adjustment is provided so that the spindle can be raised or lowered, and a second adjustment locks the spindle at any desired height above the table.

Power and Speed. The medium-size shaper using ½″ hole cutters works nicely with a ½ h.p. motor. Where large knives mounted between slotted collars are used, ¾ to 1-h.p. will give best results. The motor must be a 3450 r.p.m. type in order to give the shaper spindle the required speed. Pulleys are generally about a 3 to 1 ratio, so that the

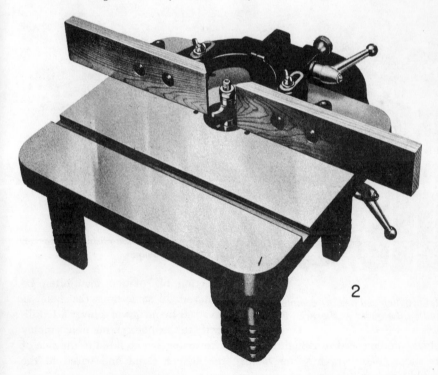

Fig. 2. Unit for bench mounting.

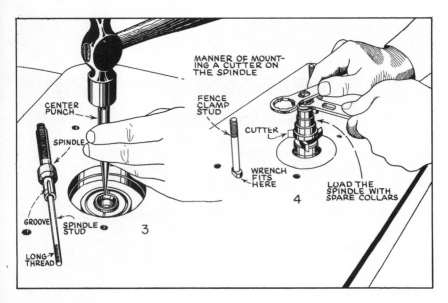

CENTER PUNCH

SPINDLE

GROOVE SPINDLE STUD

LONG THREAD

3

MANNER OF MOUNT-ING A CUTTER ON THE SPINDLE

FENCE CLAMP STUD

CUTTER

WRENCH FITS HERE

LOAD THE SPINDLE WITH SPARE COLLARS

4

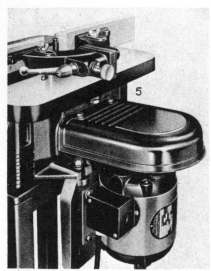

5

6

Fig. 6. Spiral spindle-raising mechanism of light-duty shaper.

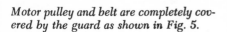

Motor pulley and belt are completely covered by the guard as shown in Fig. 5.

actual spindle speed runs slightly over or under 10,000 r.p.m. The motor should be reversible since an opposite direction of rotation may often be required. In some units the motor is reversed by means of a lever fitted directly to the motor; other units employ a reversing switch fitted to the side of the shaper stand and wired to the motor.

Use the ring guard for shaping curved work.

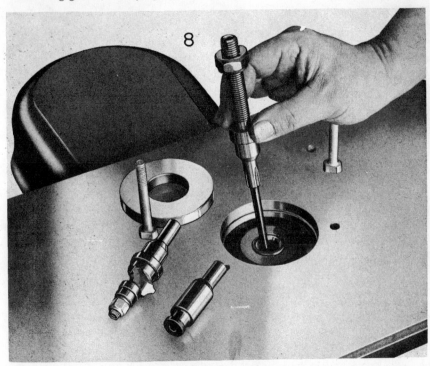

Interchangeable spindles permit use of wide variety of shaper cutters.

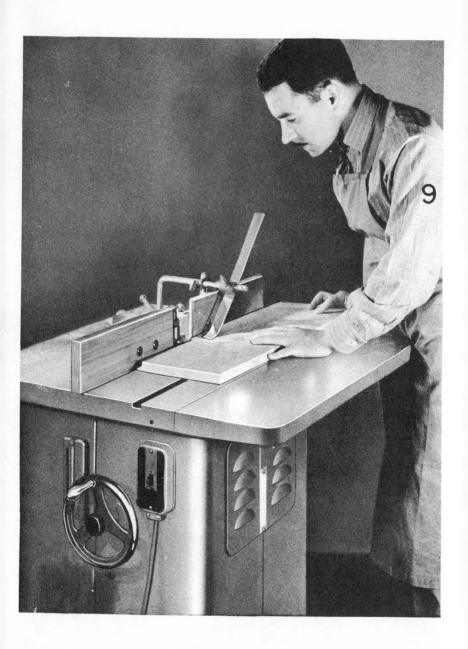

THE SHAPER . . . *Top ranking production tool for the small shop and capable of a score of different operations, some of which are impossible in any manner. Photo above illustrates cabinet model with ¾ inch spindle. The machine should be located in an unobstructed working space.*

4

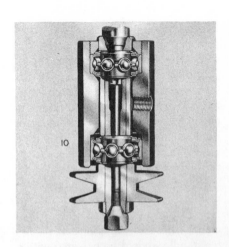

Fig. 10. Short, strong spindle and very closely spaced bearings, eliminate whip and produce chatterless work. Requires no lubrication for life of bearings.

USE A SMALL MALLET TO FREE THE SPINDLE

11

SPINDLE

PULL

STICK

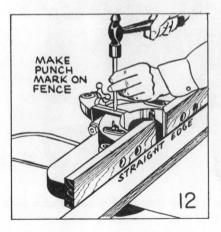

MAKE PUNCH MARK ON FENCE

STRAIGHT EDGE

12

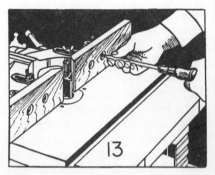

13

Auxiliary Spindles. There are four auxiliary spindles—the stub spindle for cope cutters, the ⁵⁄₁₆″ diameter spindle for cutters having this size hole, the ½″ diameter spindle for ½″ hole cutters and the ¾″ spindle for ¾″ hole cutters. The latter can be used only on the heavy-duty cabinet model shaper. Each spindle is fitted with a tie-rod, threaded at both ends. One end of the rod is fitted to the spindle while the opposite end is capped with a tapered nut after passing through the hollow main spindle. The shank of each spindle is fitted with a keyway. This engages a ball or key inside the main spindle to prevent it from turning. A light punch mark on the rim of the main spindle, as shown in Fig. 3, page 2, is an aid to locating the auxiliary spindle. Once in place, the spindle can be fitted with the necessary collars and cutters, as shown in Fig. 4. Because of accurate fitting, it may be necessary to use the method shown in Fig. 11 to remove the auxiliary spindle.

The Adjustable Fence. The fence is fitted to the shaper table by means of two studs and wingnuts. Adjustment of either half of the fence can be made when required. For most work, the two halves of the fence should be in line. A punch mark across the two parts, as shown in Fig. 12, page 5, is a useful index in re-setting. The wood face pieces of the fence are adjustable in or out to accommodate various sizes of cutters. The opening should never be any more than is required to clear the cutter. Changes in the setting are made by loosening the bolts, pushing the wood facings to the required position, and retightening, as shown in Fig. 13.

Ring Guard. The ring guard should always be used when shaping curved work directly against collars.

Besides offering protection, the guard provides a hold-down, pressing the work down on the table surface.

Sliding Jig. The sliding jig, as shown in Fig. 16, page 8, is an essential part of any shaper. Its purpose is to clamp the work securely so that it can be advanced to the cutter. It is used chiefly in returning mouldings across the ends of narrow strips.

Heavy-Duty Shaper. A phantom view of a typical heavy-duty cabinet type shaper is shown in Fig. 15. A machine of this size, swinging a ¾″ diameter spindle, should be powered with a ¾ to 1½ h.p. motor. The construction of

The entire mechanism of the cabinet shaper is one unit assembled and bolted to the bottom of the table as shown in Fig. 14.

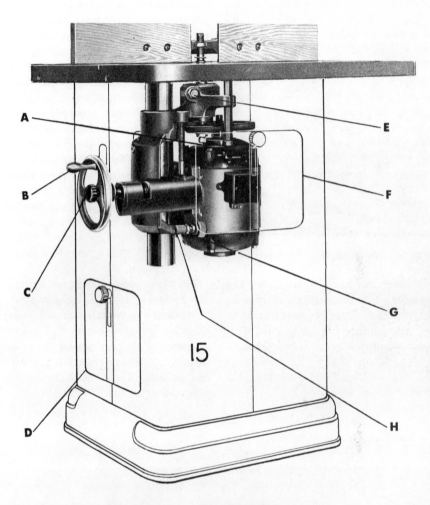

MECHANISM OF HEAVY-DUTY SHAPER

A—Spindle Tie-Rod Nut
B—Spindle Height Handwheel
C—Spindle Lock Knob
D—Cleanout Door

E—Bearing Clamp Screw
F—Removable Panel
G—Belt Tension Adjustment
H—Spindle Stop Screw

this machine differs from the lighter model previously described, the main points of departure being the spindle raising mechanism and mounting of motor, as shown in Fig. 15. The standard spindle for this machine is ¾″ in

7

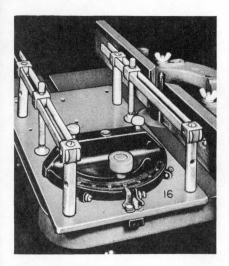

Fig. 16. The sliding jig.

Switches. All standard single-phase motors come equipped with an eight-foot long cord and plug for attachment to the lighting circuit line. If this type of motor is used, it will be necessary to disconnect this cord from the motor. For this type of motor, a toggle switch box assembly is furnished, which includes a three-foot long cord. In making this hook-up, the switch cord is fastened to the motor in place of the cord and plug which is removed from the motor, and the long cord and plug is, in turn, fastened to the switch. A reversing mechanism is provided on this type of motor which is operated by shifting the lever directly on the motor.

For three-phase motor installation, the reversing is done by a separate drum-controller switch mounted on the outside of the shaper cabinet. A switch mounting plate provides for this combination. This same plate also provides for mounting a manual starter having overload protection if desired.

diameter and has a travel of 3″. The spindle is fitted inside the main spindle, as previously described, and this method of mounting permits the use of ½″ diameter and other auxiliary spindles. The table size is 27 by 28″, which can be increased to 27 by 36″ by the addition of a back wing.

Cutters and Collars

Shaper Cutters and Collars. A wide variety of knives, saws, collars, etc., are used in shaper operation, a typical group being as shown in Figs. 1 to 10. Fig. 1 shows the standard three-lip cutter with ½" spindle hole. These are available in a wide variety of shapes and are undoubtedly the safest and most practical type of knife for average work in the small shop. Similar cutters with ⁵⁄₁₆" hole can also be used by substituting an auxiliary spindle of the proper diameter. A second type of commonly used cutter is the open face knife clamped between two slotted collars, as shown in Fig. 2. The blank knives are easily ground to any required shape. Figure 28, page

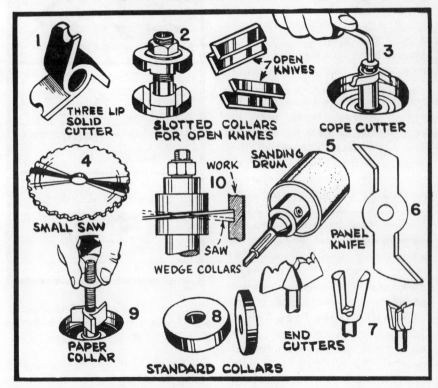

Figs. 1–10 show examples of shaper cutters and collars.

14, shows a three-knife cutter-head. A variety of ready-machined knives can be obtained, any set of which can be mounted in this head. The center hole is ¾", but a bushing permits mounting on a ½" spindle.

Fig. 3 shows a cope cutter and the special spindle on which it is carried. A small saw, Fig. 4, is a useful accessory for grooving and rough cutting. No. 5 is the familiar sanding drum. Fig. 6 shows a wing cutter, used for making raised panels and similar work. A group of end cutters are pictured in Fig. 7. These, as the name implies, travel vertically and make an end cut.

Standard shaper collars, Fig. 8, are from ⅛ to ½" thick and of various diameters to permit control over the depth of cut. Paper collars are often used as shims to build up a standard collar to some required exact size, as shown in Fig. 9. Collars of special size or construction are often made up to suit the work, a common example being the wedge collars shown in Fig. 10. A saw clamped between these collars (they can be made from hardwood) will cut a more or less wider groove than the saw thickness depending on the wedge angle of the collars. Stationary collars, which fit into the table opening, as shown in Fig. 15, and ball-bearing collars (these are simply ball races which fit over the spindle) are often used instead of standard collars to eliminate scoring, especially in production work.

Mounting Open Face Knives. Open face knives are perfectly safe to use, but only when they are properly mounted. The first step in mounting a set of knives is shown in Fig. 11. The cutter head is placed on the pin vise,

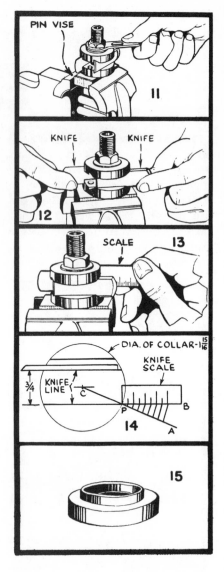

Figs. 11 to 14 show the method of mounting open face knives. Fig. 15 pictures a stationary collar.

and the nut is turned down to lightly clamp both knives. The ends of the two knives are then gripped between

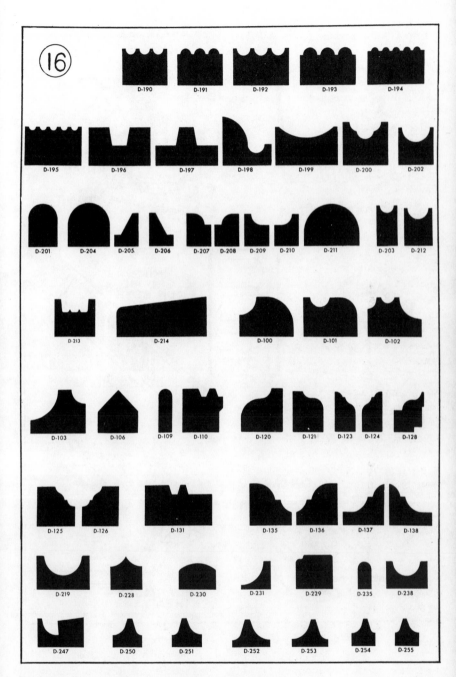

Fig. 16 pictures profiles of standard three-lip cutters.

11

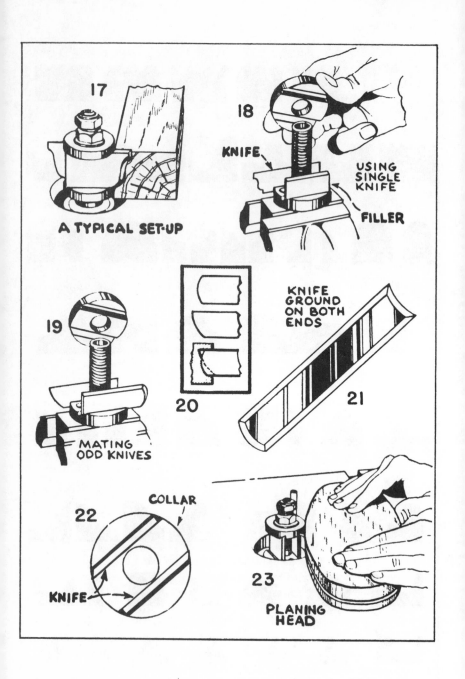

17

A TYPICAL SET-UP

18

KNIFE

USING
SINGLE
KNIFE

FILLER

19

20

KNIFE
GROUND
ON BOTH
ENDS

21

MATING
ODD KNIVES

22

COLLAR

23

KNIFE

PLANING
HEAD

Figs. 17–23 show various methods of using open knives between slotted collars.

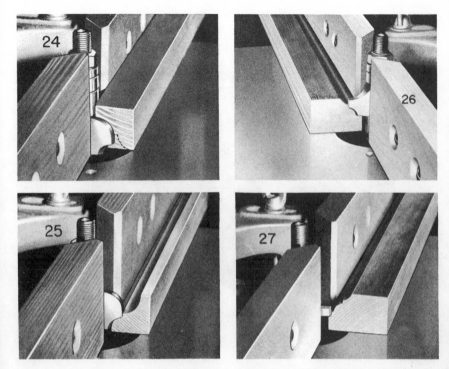

Figs. 24–27 show how cuts are combined to produce moulded shapes.

the fingers and pulled outwards. Both knives should slide with an equal tension—if one pulls more readily than the other, it is an indication that the knives are not of the same width, and *knives which are of unequal width should never be used together between slotted collars.* It can readily be seen that if one knife is a trifle narrower than the other, the wider of the two will be clamped firmly while the other will be loose and apt to fly out when the machine is set in motion. However, providing both knives are clamped evenly, the knife projection can then be measured setting both knives to project exactly equal, as shown in Fig. 13, page 10, after which the nut is turned down

tight. An ordinary thin steel rule can be used as a gauge, but the dimensions will read about $\frac{1}{32}''$ off. If a knife scale for exact measuring is required, it can be made as shown in Fig. 14. First draw a circle of the same diameter as the collar—$1\frac{15}{16}''$. On this, lay out the knife lines. Project one of the knife lines to the point B. From the center of the circle, draw a line through point P to point A. On line PA, lay off $\frac{1}{8}''$ marks from a common rule, starting at P. With C as center, extend these marks to line PB, these marks being the exact dimensions for the knife scale.

Methods of Using Open Face Knives. Open face knives can be used in a number of different manners,

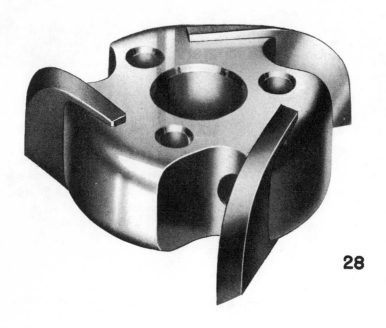

28

A variety of matched shapes are available for the three knife cutter head shown in Fig. 28. The head is made of alloy steel and fits either ½ or ¾ inch spindles.

as shown in Figs. 17 to 23, page 12. Fig. 17 shows a standard set-up, two blank knives ground to the required contour being held between the collars. For light cutting, or where the run is not long, one knife alone is often used, as shown in Fig. 18, a short blank piece of steel being used in the other slot as a filler. It is important, of course, that the filler be the same exact width as the knife. Odd knives of the same width but of different shapes are sometimes mated, as shown in Fig. 19. The moulding which would be cut in the example is shown in Fig. 20. Mating is often useful, but should not be practiced

unless both knives are approximately of the same weight. Grinding knives at both ends, Fig. 21, is widely practiced, and is especially good for cuts requiring a male and female joint. Straight knives ground to the same diameter as the cutterhead, as shown in Fig. 22 and 23, are often used for outline planing.

Combining Cuts. Knives are sometimes made to cut a required moulding in one pass of the work. More often, however, two or three passes are required, using standard shapes. Figs. 24 to 27, page 13, show typical examples of how cuts are combined to shape moulded edges.

14

Methods of Operation

Four Main Methods. There are four main methods used in shaper operation: (1) shaping with guides, (2) shaping against collars, (3) shaping with an outline pattern, (4) shaping with forms. Each of these methods is widely used, and each is adapted for a particular type of work. In the brief description of each method which follows, and in the illustrations, the same cut is shown for each, but this would not, of course, apply in actual work.

Shaping with Guides. Guides are fastened to the shaper table and form a support for the work as it is advanced to the cutter. The most common type of guide is the standard fence, **as** shown in Fig. 1. In addition to this, there are a great number of other straight fences, also concave and convex fences for curved work and special fences for odd shapes. Shaping with a guide is the safest and most satisfactory method of working, and this method should always be used when the work permits. As can be seen in the diagram, the fence is the controlling factor in limiting the depth of cut.

Shaping Against Collars. Work which cannot be shaped against a guide is usually shaped against a collar. In this method of working, the rim of the collar rides against the work and limits the depth of cut. This is one of

SHAPING WITH GUIDES

This method is most used for straight work, the guide limiting the depth of cut.

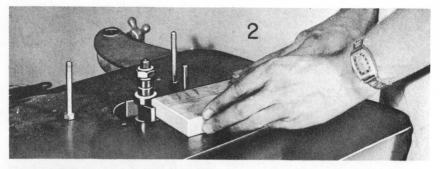

SHAPING AGAINST COLLARS

In this method of working, the diameter of the collar controls the cut.

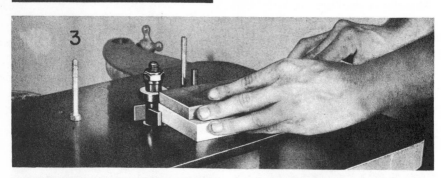

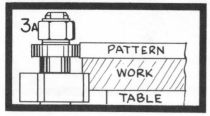

SHAPING WITH PATTERN

The pattern rides against the collar to limit the depth of cut.

the most useful methods used in shaping, its only drawback being that the revolving collar will slightly score or burn the work. This fault is not a serious objection since the scoring is usually light when the work is handled properly.

Shaping with an Outline Pattern. This is similar to shaping against collars, except that a pattern and not the work rides against the collar. Scoring is thus eliminated, and the same pat-

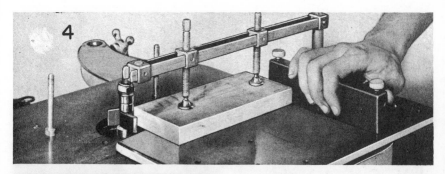

SHAPING WITH FORM

The form holds the work in position so that it can be advanced to the cutter.

tern can be used for any number of like pieces. This latter feature makes this method preferable for many shaping jobs where pieces must be produced in quantity.

Shaping with Forms. A form is any devise in which the work is held so that it can be advanced to the cutter. The most common form is the sliding jig, and it is this form which is shown in the picture, Fig. 4. (The supporting arm has been painted out to show the cut more plainly.)

Setting the Cutter. In making any moulded edge, the pattern is usually marked on the end of the work. The proper cutter is then mounted on the spindle, after which the spindle is raised or lowered to the proper height. This is done with either the spiral adjustment, Fig. 5, or with the spindle-raising handwheel, Fig. 6, depending on the machine. The fence is then located to give the right depth of cut, as shown in Fig. 7. Where collars are

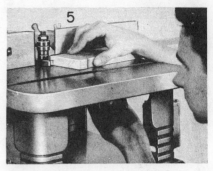

The spindle is raised or lowered to the proper height using the spiral adjustment, Fig. 5, or with the hand wheel, Fig 6, on cabinet model shapers.

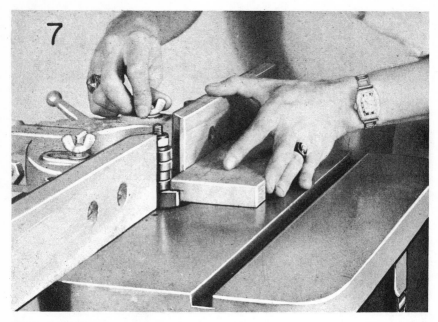

The work is held against the cutter so that proper fence settings can be made as shown in Fig. 7.

used, the collar is checked against the work in a similar manner.

Rotation and Feed. The recommended spindle speed for small cutters is 10,000 r.p.m. The shaper is usually fitted with a reversing switch so that the cutter can rotate in either direction. Whatever the direction, the work must be advanced INTO and AGAINST the cutter. Feeding from the right side of the machine is preferred by most workers, the rotation of the cutter being counter-clockwise, as shown in Fig. 8. When the work is fed from the left side, the cutter rotates in a clockwise direction, as shown in Fig. 9.

When returning mouldings or cutting all edges of a piece, the first cut should be made on end grain, each edge being taken in turn so that the

final cut is with the grain, as shown in Fig. 10.

The direction of feed should be such that the cutter will cut with the grain, as shown by the two examples at the top of Fig. 11. This is of minor importance if the shaper is a high-speed machine, but of increasing importance with slower speed spindles.

The feed is often fixed by the nature of the work. That is, in planing a straight edge, the worker could feed from either the left or right side of the machine. On some shapes, however, the cut can only be made in one direction. An example is shown in Fig. 11. Here we have a moulding on which it is required to make the cut shown by the dotted line. The cutter to be used and its position on the spindle as

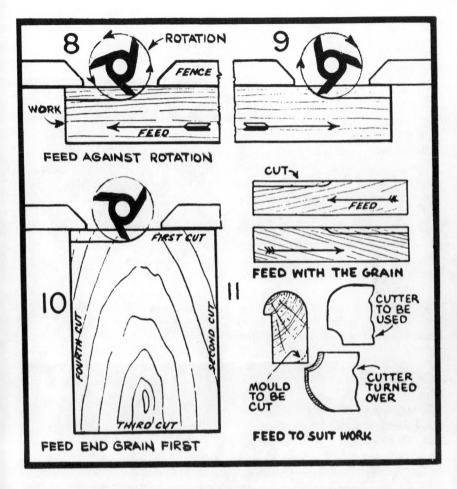

8 ROTATION FENCE
WORK
FEED
FEED AGAINST ROTATION

9

10
FIRST CUT
FOURTH CUT
SECOND CUT
THIRD CUT
FEED END GRAIN FIRST

CUT
FEED
FEED WITH THE GRAIN

11
MOULD TO BE CUT
CUTTER TO BE USED
CUTTER TURNED OVER
FEED TO SUIT WORK

Figs. 8–11 show fundamentals of feed in relation to rotation of cutter.

viewed from the right side of the machine is shown at the top of the diagram. It is apparent that the work cannot be fed from the right. Now, by turning the cutter over, and feeding from the left side of the machine, the required mould can be cut. Many cuts of this nature make it apparent why the shaper must have a reversing switch for satisfactory operation.

CHAPTER FOUR

Shaping with Guides

Definition. A shaper guide is any wood or metal fixture or fence which can be clamped or otherwise fastened to the shaper table in such a position as to form a guide for the work. The most common guide is the straight fence. It can be adjustable or non-adjustable, and varies considerably in construction, as will be seen in the following paragraphs. Curved fences are also used extensively as guides for circular and segment work. In every case, the guide is fixed, the work slid-

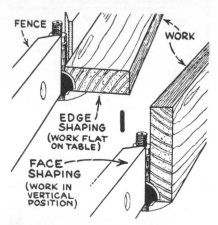

Using the standard adjustable fence for straight shaping is shown in Fig. 2.

ing along it to meet the cutter. When the work is advanced with its edge against the fence, the operation is known as edge shaping; when the work is advanced with its face against the fence, the operation is called face shaping, as shown in Fig. 1. Edge shaping is always preferred because of the better bearing surface thus afforded.

The Adjustable Fence. The small shaper is usually fitted with an adjustable fence of the type pictured and described on page 5. The whole fence is readily adjusted in relation to the spindle to expose the cutter to the proper depth for the moulding required, as can be seen in the Fig. 2. A second adjustment permits either half of the fence to be advanced or retracted. For average work where a portion of the original edge of the work is not touched by the cutter, as shown by the examples at the top of Fig. 3, both the front and rear fences are in a straight line. The distance which the fence is set back from the cutting circle is the depth of cut, as shown in the diagram.

Where the shaping operation removes the entire edge of the wood, as, for examples, in jointing or making a full bead, it can readily be seen that the shaped edge will not be supported by the fence when both fences are in line. In this case, the work is advanced to the approximate position shown in the center diagram, Fig. 3, after which the shaper is stopped and the rear fence advanced to lightly contact the wood. It can be seen that the rear fence is thus in line with the cutting circle, and this adjustment can be made, if desired, before the actual shaping operation begins.

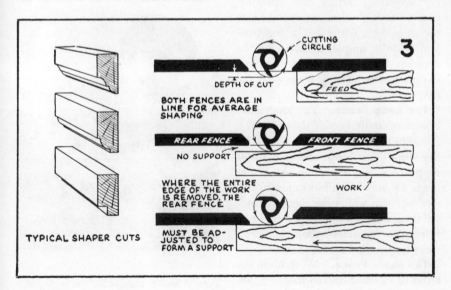

TYPICAL SHAPER CUTS

CUTTING CIRCLE

3

DEPTH OF CUT

BOTH FENCES ARE IN LINE FOR AVERAGE SHAPING

FEED

REAR FENCE

FRONT FENCE

NO SUPPORT

WHERE THE ENTIRE EDGE OF THE WORK IS REMOVED, THE REAR FENCE

WORK

MUST BE ADJUSTED TO FORM A SUPPORT

Fig. 3 shows how the shaper fence must be adjusted for making various cuts.

Fig. 4. *Shaping circular work without the use of a segment fence.*

The High Fence. Wide stock which must be face shaped is sometimes difficult to guide along the comparatively low standard fence, and to secure a better bearing surface most operators prefer the high auxiliary wood fence shown in Figs. 5 and 6. The construction is quite simple, as shown in the diagram, the base affording a landing so that the fence can be clamped to the shaper table.

The Long Fence. The long fence is somewhat similar, as shown in Fig. 7, except that the base forms a table for the work. This fence makes a better support for long work, and also allows the fastening of stop blocks for fluting, reeding, etc., which the shorter standard fence does not always permit. Long work in a "one-man" shop should always be handled in this manner.

The Miter Fence. Work to be mitered or beveled on the shaper is advanced past the cutter on a suitable miter fence, a typical form of construction being shown in Fig. 8. Where the edge of the work is already beveled, the fence is constructed with the fence proper in a vertical position, as shown in the left circle inset. Where the edge of the work is square, the fence is vertical in relation to the table of the complete unit. Made in this manner, the fence supports the work both before and after leaving the cutter. By using hinges and a simple quadrant, the fence or table, or both, could be ar-

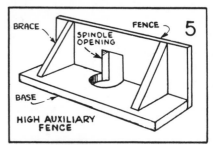

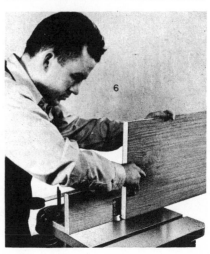

Figs. 5 and 6 show how the high fence simplifies face shaping of wide stock.

22

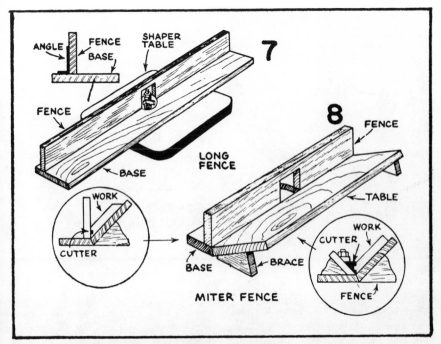

Figs. 7 and 8 show construction of long and miter fences.

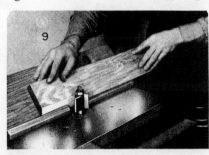

Fig. 9 shows miter fence being used in beveling an edge.

ranged to assume any required angle, an important feature in shaping segment work. A jig of this nature is described on page 46. Fig. 9 illustrates a typical miter fence in action, beveling an edge of one of the pieces in a built-up column.

The Segment Fence. The segment or circular fence is a useful guide in shaping segment or circular work. The work must be a true circle or a segment of a true circle, the fence being useless for curved work which is not circular. Fig. 10, page 24, shows the set-up of a segment fence for making an inside cut. The guide is simply a flat piece of stock clamped to the shaper table. The radius of the fence and that of the work must be exactly the same. The work is advanced to the cutter in the same manner used for straight work. Where the whole edge of the work is to be removed, the after portion of the guide must be made the required distance fuller to contact the work.

A segment fence for outside cuts is shown in Fig. 11. It can be seen that

23

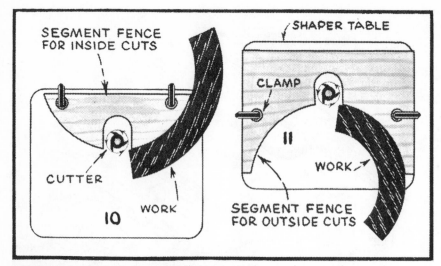

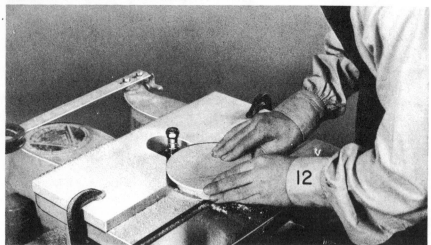

Figs. 10–13 show construction and manner of using segment guides for curved and circular work.

both fences can be cut from a single board. It must be remembered, however, that a new fence is necessary for every new-diameter work, and that the fence must be cut to the same radius as the work. Smoothness of both guide and work is required for satisfactory operation.

An excellent guide which can be used for a wide variety of different-diameter circles is shown in Fig. 12. This consists of a flat guide with a 90° vee opening cut in the center. A little consideration will show that the sides

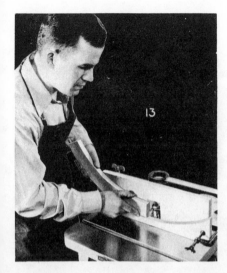

of this opening will afford two contact points for circular work of any size up to the capacity of the guide. This guide cannot be used for segment work, since the cut at the beginning and end would not be supported.

Fig. 13 shows a segment guide being used for face shaping. The method of working is the same as before, except that the segment is clamped upright to the high fence. The photo shows the end of the cut, the worker having gradually changed his position from the side to the rear of the machine to permit readier handling of the stock, such body movements being necessary in many shaper operations.

Other Guides. Other guides, fences, shoot-boards, etc., can be made up as the need for them arises. For general work, the standard adjustable fence serves every purpose. For faster production work or increased safety in operation, the auxiliary fence will often work out to better advantage. The few examples shown here do not

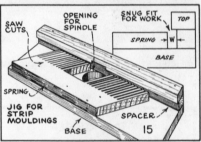

Fig. 14 pictures the strip jig in use. Fig. 15 shows its construction.

exhaust the subject, but are simply intended to illustrate the general principles of design to serve as a basis for making other guides. Many of the guides become permanent fixtures and should be saved; others may be discarded after the job for which they were made has been completed. Permanent jigs should be well-made, sanded and varnished. Instead of being clamped to the table, they can be readily constructed to fasten with the same studs which are used to hold the standard fence in position.

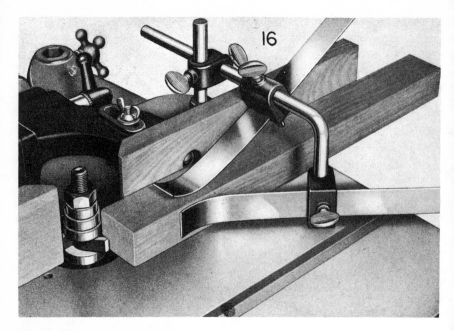

The standard spring type hold down is shown in Fig. 16.

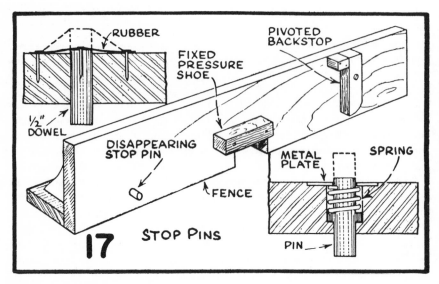

RUBBER

PIVOTED
BACKSTOP

FIXED
PRESSURE
SHOE

½"
DOWEL

DISAPPEARING
STOP PIN

METAL
PLATE

SPRING

FENCE

17 STOP PINS

PIN

Production guide fitted with pressure shoe and stops: two styles of disappearing stops are shown in Fig. 17.

Hold-downs. Any device which holds the work against the fence or the shaper table is known as a hold-down. There are many different styles of hold-downs—wheels, weighted arms, spring tensioners, etc.—all of which serve the same general purpose of keeping the work in close contact with the table or fence. Very often the hold-down is built into and is a part of the guide, a typical example being the guide shown in Figs. 14 and 15, page 25. This shows a jig for narrow mouldings, commonly called strip mouldings, which is so constructed that the work is at all times supported against the impact of the cutter, the wood spring holding the *work in* while the top piece of the jig holds it *down*. The same effect is secured through the use of standard shaper hold-downs—thin, steel springs which can be readily adjusted to fit any size of average work. Any hold-down is more effective when it supports the work at a point slightly behind the point of cutting, as shown in Fig. 16. Suitable mountings on the standard shaper fence permits the hold-down to be used at either end to correspond with the direction of feed. Mountings for the standard hold-downs can be readily fitted to most auxiliary guides, or these guides can be fitted with wood springs or the simpler fixed pressure shoe, as shown in the Fig. 17. Some form of hold-down should always be used whenever possible.

Stops. Stops must be used to control the travel of the work in doing such operations as grooving, fluting and reeding, where the cut does not extend the full length of the work. The simplest method is to use scrap pieces of wood, clamping these to the fence at the required positions. Where production work is being done, a more permanent set-up is usually desirable, something on the order of the guide shown in the drawing. The stop or stops on the front or infeed portion of the guide are usually of the disappearing type, since this style does not interfere with ordinary straight shaping when the stop is not used.

There are two styles of disappearing stops shown in the diagram, one using a rubber band and the other a spring to project the stop forward through the fence. The backstop is usually pivoted or hinged so that it can be swung out of the way when not in use. It is evident that each set of stops is used for just one particular operation, and is of no use for anything else.

CHAPTER FIVE

Shaping with Collars

Working Conditions. Certain conditions must always prevail when work is shaped directly against guide collars: (1) Collars must be smooth and true, free from all gum or other substances. They should be inspected frequently during long runs since some woods will deposit a layer of hard pitch on the rim of the collar as thick as $\frac{1}{16}''$, and this in a very few hours. The gum is easily removed with a stiff bristle brush and benzine or gasoline. (2) The edge of the work to be shaped must be smoothed to net size. It can be seen that any irregularity in the surface which rides against the collar will be duplicated on the moulded surface. (3) A portion of the edge of the work must remain untouched by the cutters in order that the collar will have a sufficient bearing surface. (4) The work must be fairly heavy in proportion to the cut being made. Under no circumstances should short work of light body be shaped against collars. These four rules—smooth work, clean collars, riding edge, and body of the work—are shown in Figs. 1 to 4, and it is important for good work and for safety in operation that they be strictly observed when doing shaper work of this nature.

Position of Collar. The collar may be used either above, below, or between two cutters, as shown in Figs. 5, 6 and 7, page 29. The advantage in having the cutter uppermost, Fig. 5, lies mainly in the fact that the progress of the cut can thus be observed at all times. Where the collar is uppermost, Fig. 6, the cut cannot be seen, yet this method offers some advantage in that the cut is not affected by slight variations in the thickness of the stock; also, accidental lifting of the work will not

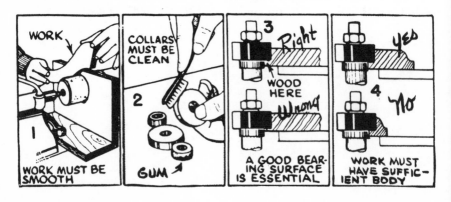

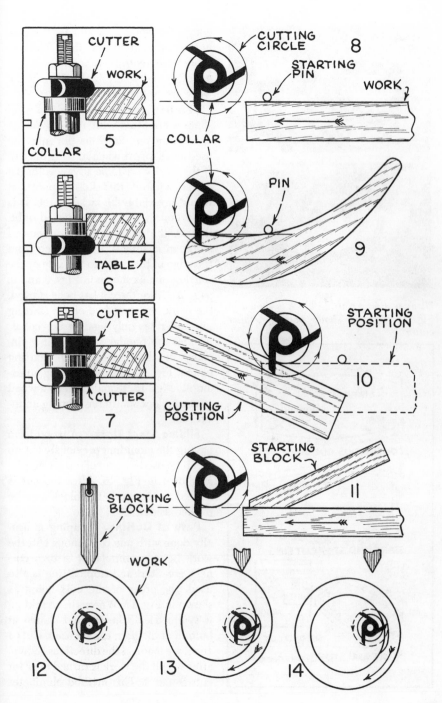

CUTTER
WORK
COLLAR
5

CUTTING CIRCLE
8
STARTING PIN
WORK
COLLAR

TABLE
6

COLLAR
PIN
9

CUTTER
CUTTER
7

STARTING POSITION
CUTTING POSITION
10

STARTING BLOCK
STARTING BLOCK
11

WORK

12   13   14

Using a sliding starting block is shown in Fig. 16. Fig. 17 shows path of shaper cutter.

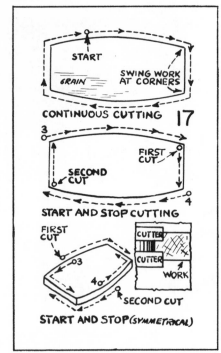

gouge the wood as would be the case in the first method described. The collar-between-cutters is a method frequently used where both edges of the work are to be moulded.

Starting the Cut. Practically all shapers are fitted with a steel fulcrum or starting pin, and this pin must be used as a support when starting the cut. If the work were to be advanced to the cutter without this side support, it would invariably be kicked back. It is important that the cut be started right, that is, the wood must be advanced along an imaginary line running from the edge of the collar to the side of the starting pin, as shown in Figs. 8 and 9, page 29. After the cut has been started, the work is swung free of the starting pin and rides only against the collar. Besides the regular steel starting pin, many workers use wood starting blocks, Fig. 11 on page 29 being an example. Figs. 12, 13 and 14 show a wood starting block set up for running an inside cut.

Sliding Start Block. A wood form having the moulding previously cut on it can be used instead of a starting pin, as shown in Fig. 16. After the cut is started on the work, the block may be pushed aside.

Path of Cutting. Shaping is usually done with one continuous cut, the work being manipulated to turn corners, etc. Start and stop cutting is also used, the order of the cuts being as shown in Fig. 17. Where the moulding is symmetrical, the method shown at bottom of diagram can be used. Cuts 1 and 2 are made in the directions shown, after which the work is turned over for cuts 3 and 4. This method eliminates

A wood guide block is necessary when shaping compound curves as shown in Figs. 18 and 19.

running off the end grain.

Compound Curves. Work with compound curves must sometimes be shaped, an example being the head rail on a chair. Fig. 18 shows the set-up. This is simply a block of wood, with the top surface cut to a curve a little sharper than the curve of the work. This guide block is nailed to a second block, the under block being clamped to the shaper table. The crown of the guide block should be in line with the center of the spindle. The spindle is usually raised as far as it will go for work of this kind, and the cutter is mounted high, with just room enough above for the guide collar and nut. The height is necessary, of course, in order that the ends of the piece being shaped will clear the table.

Shaping is done much the same as if the work were a flat piece of wood. The top of the guide block limits the face cut, while the spindle collar limits the edge cut. The work is pushed straight across the table, being tilted slightly so that the work at the cutting point is always approximately level with the table. Over-cutting is impossible. On some curves it may be necessary to go over the work twice in order to get a full shape. Notice that the knife is set to cut on the underside of the work. Do not attempt free-hand shaping with overhanging cutters as this is both dangerous and liable to produce inaccurate work. Operated as described, that is with the cutter under the work, the cut is always accurate and the operation safe.

Shaping with Patterns

Advantages. Shaping with the use of patterns offers two outstanding advantages: (1) It permits the working of the entire edge of irregular curved objects, an operation which is impossible in any other manner. (2) It provides one of the cleanest and fastest methods of doing production work possible on any machine.

The Pattern. The average pattern is made from wood, the usual stock being ¾″ or ⅞″ thick. Small patterns are usually cut from solid stock; larger ones are best built up from suitable pieces of hardwood. Production patterns are often made from fiber in order to better withstand the continual riding against the guide collar, but for average work hardwood serves nicely. The shape of the pattern is the exact outline of the work which is to be moulded. The edges must be smooth and clean, and should be oiled to permit smooth running. Softwood patterns for production work should be edged with strip fiber, as shown in Fig. 3.

The work which is to be shaped is roughly sawn about ¹⁄₁₆″ to ⅛″ oversize, and is fastened to the pattern by means of anchor points. The simplest anchor point is the brad or nail—others are made from glazier's points, screws or bolts, as shown in the sketch. A flat point is preferable to a round point. Flat points should be inserted in the

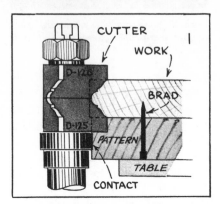

Fig. 1 shows manner of assembly to work.

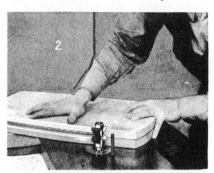

Fig. 2 shows outline pattern in use.

pattern in such a manner that they will fit lengthwise with the grain.

Examples of Work. A typical example of work done with an outline pattern is shown in Figs. 1 and 2. The

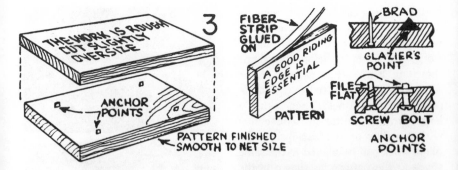

THE WORK IS ROUGH CUT SLIGHTLY OVERSIZE

ANCHOR POINTS

← PATTERN FINISHED SMOOTH TO NET SIZE

3

FIBER STRIP GLUED ON

A GOOD RIDING EDGE IS ESSENTIAL

PATTERN

BRAD

GLAZIER'S POINT

FILE FLAT

SCREW BOLT

ANCHOR POINTS

pattern in this case is a solid piece of ¾" stock, carefully smoothed to net size. The pattern, with the work attached, is advanced to the cutter the same as for shaping against guide collars. The pattern rides a suitable-diameter collar to control the cut to the proper depth, the surplus wood on the work being re moved as the moulding is cut. Fig. 1 shows the set-up being used in the photo Fig. 2. The dotted lines indicate the original size of both the pattern and the work. Notice that a portion of the pattern edge is also removed while the moulding is being cut. This, of course, is not always the case, but simply so happens for this particular cut.

Fig. 6 shows a larger table top being shaped with the use of a built-up pattern. It will also be apparent that for symmetrical shapes such as this that only a portion of the full pattern need be used if the run does not justify the making of a whole pattern. Fig. 4 makes this point clear. It can be seen that the partial pattern can be used for both ends of the table top, while the sides can be shaped against the regular straight fence. The cut being made in the photograph is diagrammed in Fig. 5, a collar the same

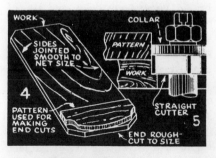

WORK

SIDES JOINTED SMOOTH TO NET SIZE

PATTERN USED FOR MAKING END CUTS

4

COLLAR

PATTERN

WORK

STRAIGHT CUTTER

END ROUGH-CUT TO SIZE

5

6

Using a built-up outline pattern for shaping the edge of a small table top is shown in Fig. 6.

diameter as cutter being used to dress a portion of the edge of the work to the same size as the pattern. A shaped cutter used with a smaller collar would then be used to cut the moulding.

Outline Planing. It can be seen from the foregoing description that outline planing can be readily done on the shaper. That is, certain shapes can be planed directly from square-sawed stock, an example being the shape shown in Fig. 7. The pattern of the required outline is fitted to a suitable piece of blank stock. Then, using a large straight cutter in connection with a collar of the same size, the blank stock can be planed to the same shape as the pattern, as shown in the Fig. 7. Excessively deep cuts are, of course, to be avoided in view of possible spindle strain, but ½″ cuts in ¾″ stock and deeper cuts in lighter work can be made quite easily.

Double Patterns. Where symmetrical mouldings are being cut, a double pattern with the work sandwiched between is sometimes useful, as shown in Fig. 8. The advantage lies in the fact that the work can be turned over at any time in order to favor the grain. While it is true that a high spindle speed makes grain of little importance, reversing in this manner is sometimes useful.

Register Blocks. Register blocks are used for production work, their purpose being to afford a quick and simple means of fitting the work to the pattern or patterns in the proper position, as shown in Fig. 9. Quite often, a hole in the work or a projecting lug can be used to good advantage to get the pattern in proper register.

Bevel Planing. In some classes of work, the frames for vee-bottom boats being a typical example, require the beveling of an edge which often varies, being at a greater angle at one end than the other. Where production work of this nature must be done, a great

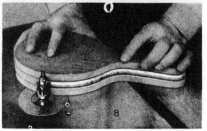

Figs. 7 and 8 show outline planing and use of double form.

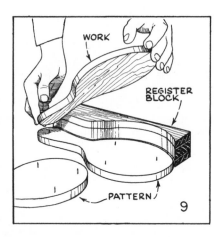

Fig. 9 explains register blocks.

savings in time as well as perfection in results can be effected by making a double pattern to the required shape and bevel. Work is clamped between the two patterns and the whole unit

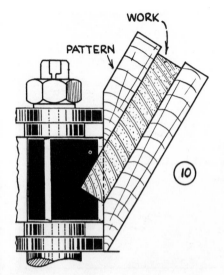

WORK

PATTERN

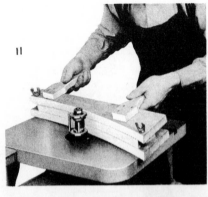

Fig. 10 pictures the action of the cutter. Fig. 11 shows bevel planing the edge of a boat frame part by using a double pattern with the work clamped between.

fed to a straight cutter, the patterns riding collars of the same diameter as the cutter, as shown in Figs. 10 and 11.

Double Edge Patterns. Where long, narrow shapes are to be planed to size, the use of a conventional form becomes more or less unsatisfactory. The main drawback to the use of a regular form for such work is the safety factor—it can be seen that such shapes as those shown in Fig. 13, offer little room for anchor points and must necessarily pass the feed hand very close to the knife.

A better type of pattern for such work is made from a wide board carrying the outline of the work on opposite edges. The typical example illustrated in Figs. 14 to 17 show how a double-edge pattern for a chair leg is made

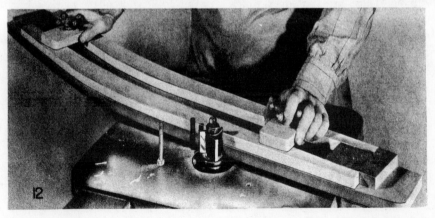

Fig. 12 shows how a pattern with double edges affords a safe, accurate method of handling narrow pieces.

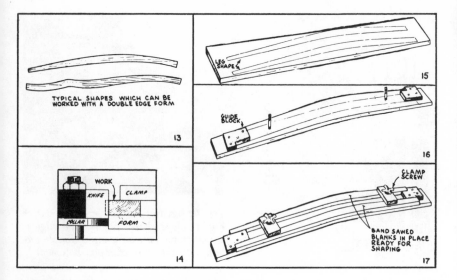

TYPICAL SHAPES WHICH CAN BE
WORKED WITH A DOUBLE EDGE FORM

13

LEG
SHAPE

15

GUIDE
BLOCK

16

WORK

KNIFE   CLAMP

COLLAR   FORM

14

CLAMP
SCREW

BAND SAWED
BLANKS IN PLACE
READY FOR
SHAPING

17

and used. A board 6″ or 8″ wide and slightly longer than the work is required. On opposite edges of this is penciled the full shape of the work, as shown in Fig. 15. This should be done from an accurate wood or metal pattern. The outer line of each leg shape is then band sawed and the edges carefully smoothed and lightly sponged with oil. These are the edges which will ride against the guide collar. Guide blocks are made to fit the ends of the inside lines, and are nailed or screwed in place, as shown in Fig. 16. Fig. 17 shows two of the band sawed blanks in place ready for shaping. One edge of each is shaped in the position shown, then the legs are reversed from side to side and the opposite edges cut to size.

In band sawing the blanks, the saw cut should be made carefully for a distance of about two inches from each end, while the rest of the cut can run run up to ⅛″ wide of the mark. It can be seen that a fairly accurate end cut is necessary in order that the blanks will be located at the proper positions when fitted against the guide blocks.

CHAPTER SEVEN

The Use of Forms

Definition. A form is any device or jig in or upon which the work is securely fastened by means of clamps, screws or wedges so that it can be advanced to the cutter. In this classification are included the sliding jig and the tenoning jig, but the term is more truly applied to special forms which must be used to support odd-shaped work. Since the construction of the latter type of form requires both a money and time expenditure in making, it is used only when the work cannot be shaped by other methods. It can be seen that this condition does not apply to the various all-purpose forms, such as the sliding and tenoning jigs, the fluting jig, etc. Indeed, in this case, the jig offers the simplest and least expensive method of working.

The Tenoning Jig. This fixture, made especially for making tenons on the circular saw, can be used to good advantage in various shaper operations, especially where narrow stock must be face shaped. A typical example of the work is shown in Fig. 1 where the jig is being used to hold a drawer side for grooving. A backing block, as shown in the inset, is used in order to set the work within range of the cutter. The block is easily fastened to the face of the jig by means of screws inserted through holes provided for this purpose. Another example of the tenon

jig in use is shown in Fig. 4, page 38. The backing block block is not necessary in this case. It can easily be seen that the tenoning jig offers the most satisfactory set-up for making the particular type of cut shown.

The Sliding Jig. The sliding jig is a standard shaper accessory, and is indispensable for various kinds of work, especially for returning a moulding on narrow stock, as shown in Fig. 2, page 38. It is also useful for making joints, either straight or at any specified angle, as can be seen in Fig. 3. Fig. 5 shows the sliding jig being used with a 45°

BACKING BLOCK FITTED TO TENONING JIG

Fig. 1 shows how the circular saw tenoning jig can be used to good advantage for many shaper operations.

Using the sliding jig in returning a moulding is shown in Fig. 2

Fig. 3 shows the jig being used to cut a 45° miter joint.

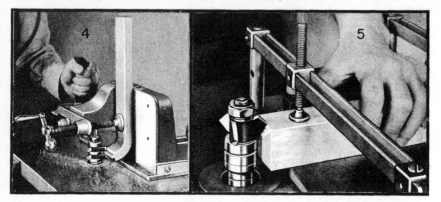

Figs. 4 and 5 show typical examples of shaper work using the tenoning and sliding jigs.

cutter, the operation being the beveling of a square post. The sliding jig is to the shaper what the miter gage is to the circular saw, and its application to a hundred-and-one jobs will readily become apparent under actual working conditions. It should always be used when end working narrow stock.

A Typical Form. Figs. 6 and 7 picture the operation and set-up for a job requiring the use of a form. The work is a cabriole leg which has been band sawed and sanded to the proper shape. The final touch is to round the outside corner, and it is this operation which is being done on the shaper. It can be seen that the work cannot be advanced

along the fence, neither can it be shaped against collars or by the use of the sliding or tenoning jigs. Hence, the need of a form to properly support the work. The edge to be shaped forms a straight line, so all that is necessary is a means of blocking the leg so that this edge will be level with the shaper table. The base of the form is shaped to the required outline, much the same as for flat pattern work. With the leg firmly blocked in place, the form is advanced to the cutter, the form riding a suitable collar. The cutter is special, being ground to the concave shape required from a straight cutter.

While on the subject of the cabriole

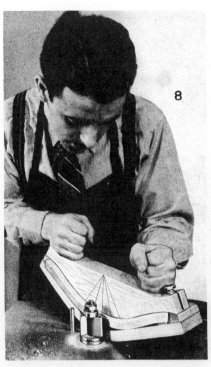

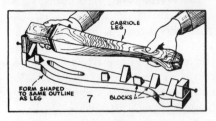

Figs. 6 and 7 show application of form in shaping odd-shaped work.

Edge shaping a chair-back rail with the use of a rocking form is shown in Fig. 8.

leg, it may be pointed out that the full shape of the leg could be readily worked with straight knives in the same manner as described for outline planing, page 33. The work would be roughly band sawed to remove excess wood, and then planed smooth to net size with an outline pattern. The work might or might not require blocking, depending upon the nature of the leg shape. A leg with shallow curves could be advanced to the cutter directly on the table surface; deeper curves would need blocking in order to give the work sufficient support.

Rocking Forms. Curved work which is to be planed to an outline is

often beyond the capacity of the cutters. An example is shown in Fig. 9—a rail in a chair back. The flat sides have been previously shaped to the required curve, either by steaming or by bandsawing. It remains to shape one edge of the piece, the curve being shown in Fig. 9, this being a picture of the finished job. Referring to Fig. 10, page 40, it can be seen that if the work is blocked in the conventional position, the cut required will be 2¾"—greater than any straight cutting edge which can be carried on the spindle. If, however half the work is advanced on one plane and the remaining half on another plane, as shown in Fig. 11, the depth of cut will then be only 1⅛", which is well within the capacity of the spindle.

Hence, the need of a rocking form. In every respect except one, this is the same as a flat form, the base carrying the outline pattern on its edge and the required blocking on its flat surface. The difference lies in the fact that the bottom is in two planes, joined by a slow curve so that the form can be rocked from one plane to the other, as shown in Fig. 12. Fig. 13 shows the work securely clamped in the form, ready for the shaping operation. Fig. 8, page 39, shows the cut in progress. The outline pattern is net size. Consequently, a collar the same diameter as the cutter is used to ride the outline pattern. The work is started against the starting pin in the usual manner and advanced to the cutter with the base of the form flat on the table. As the work nears the

center of the cut, the form must be evenly and smoothly rolled from the starting flat plane to the finishing flat plane. On concave shapes, the roll can be done quite easily; on convex curves, such as in this particular example, the roll must be made fairly evenly in order to keep the work at right angles to the cutter. As an aid to making an even roll, radial lines are drawn on the upper portion of the form, each successive line being kept vertical as that portion of the cut is pushed past the cutter.

The Fluting Jig. The fluting jig is a form familiar to most workers. It is essentially a small lathe, in which the work is held for shaper operations. A common and simple type of construction is shown in Fig. 8, page 46. The fluting jig is mostly used for fluting, hence its name. This operation is shown in Figs. 14, 15 and 16. A form of the same contour as the leg is fastened to the jig, the form riding a depth collar in the same manner as for other shaping operations. In the example shown, the flutes are being cut on a tapered surface, hence the form is simply a straight tapered piece of wood. Where the flut-

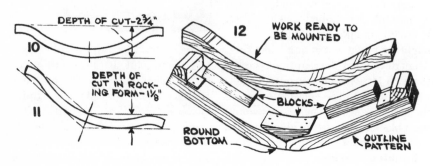

Figs. 10 to 12 show the construction of a rocking form.

ing is being done on a curved surface, the form or pattern would, of course, be of the same shape as the contour of the leg. Fig. 16 shows outside stops being used to limit the starting and stopping position of the cut. In Fig. 17, page 42, which illustrates a reeding cutter being used, the inside stops set the limits of the cut. These stops, as will be evident, start and finish against a collar to set the length of the cut. The work, in this case, is a round cylinder, so that no form is necessary, the depth collar simply riding the straight edge of the jig. Stops are also worked directly on the form itself, the pattern curving out to limit the cut. Some workers ride the work directly against the collar to limit the cut, but this method is not recommended because of its tendency to score the work.

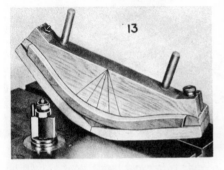

Fig. 13 shows application of the rocking form.

Square Turnings. Fig. 18 shows the fluting jig being used to work a

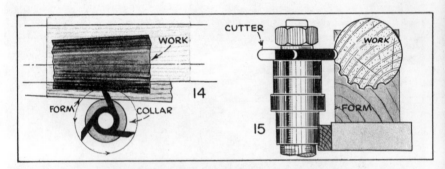

Figs. 14 and 15 show how the form rides the collar to limit the depth of cut.

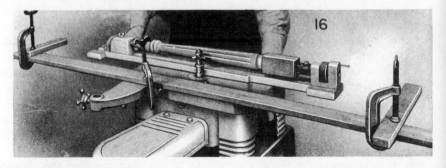

Fig. 16 shows the fluting jig being used to make flutes in a table leg.

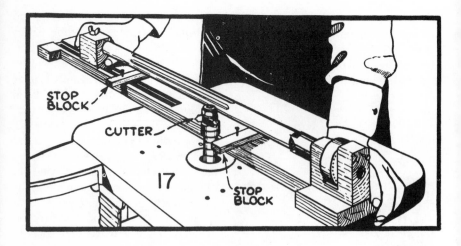

Fig. 17 shows the jig being used with a reeding cutter and inside stops to limit the cut.

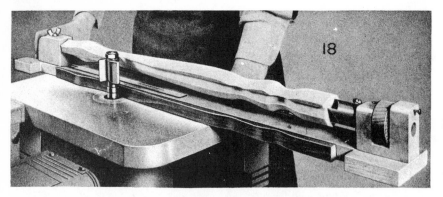

Fig. 18 shows the fluting jig being used to hold work for square turning.

square turning. This type of leg has eight or more planes shaped to a specified contour. The shape is worked directly from square stock with the use of an outline pattern fastened to the base of the jig. The example shown is a twelve-sided square turning, the cut being the next to the last to complete the leg. Square turnings are easily and quickly fashioned on the shaper in this manner, and, despite the fact that the contour is limited to a series of slow curves, the leg readily lends itself to many projects in furniture construction. It is one of the fastest methods of making legs, requiring only that the stock be sawed square and to length, after which the necessary cuts can be made on the shaper. It can be seen that it is impossible to make any concave cut of less diameter than the cutting circle of the cutter, and this should be borne in mind when planning the design. Some pleasing variations can be made by using slightly curved cutters instead of straight knives.

Caution. It is important that any form used in shaper work be well made. It must hold the work securely and have a firm base on which to slide. Never use a make-shift form in an attempt to speed up the job—do it right or not at all. This is especially important in the construction and use of rocking forms, where the proper manipulation of the form is hazardous enough in itself without adding extra dangers through poor construction of the form.

CHAPTER EIGHT

Jigs and Fixtures

Jig used for making round tenons on the ends of square stock is shown in Figs. 1 and 2.

Tenons. Round tenons are frequently necessary on the ends of square stock, and, barring a comparatively long lathe operation, the job presents considerable difficulties. However, the shaper offers an easy solution, and once the jig has been made, the stock can be tenoned quickly and safely. The jig, as shown in Fig. 1 and 2, consists of a heavy block of wood mounted over the cutter. In this block is fitted a round plug, the plug in turn having a square hole to take the work. A piece of plywood on the underside of the block allows the work to pass through but keeps the plug in place. Work to be tenoned is inserted through the square hole and into contact with the revolving cutter. A wood collar on the spindle limits the depth of cut. The work is slowly rotated, in the same direction as the rotation of the cutter, to form the complete round. Various plugs with different-size square holes can be made to suit a wide variety of work. Round stock can be tenoned in the same general manner, but a plug is unnecessary in this case, the stock simply being inserted through a round hole cut in the overhead wood block. In every case, the length of the tenon will be the same as the width of the straight cutter used. Another method of cutting tenons on round stock is shown in Fig. 3. This has one advantage in that the tenon can be tapered, often necessary as when making rake and hoe handles and in similar work.

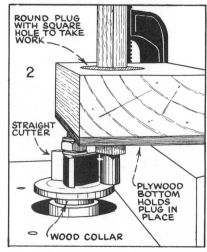

ROUND PLUG WITH SQUARE HOLE TO TAKE WORK

2

STRAIGHT CUTTER

PLYWOOD BOTTOM HOLDS PLUG IN PLACE

WOOD COLLAR

Column Work. Column work demands an adjustable bevel jig, one which can be quickly and accurately set to the proper bevel for any particular type of column. A jig of this type is shown in Figs. 6 and 7, page 46. Its general construction and use should be apparent. In making the various marks on the wood or metal arm, the table portion of the jig is set to the required angle and a corresponding mark is made on the arm, level with the top of the shaper table. To reset the jig to any particular angle, it is only necessary to set the mark on the arm level with the top of the shaper table. The angles shown are for 4, 5, 6, 8, 10, and 12-sided figures, but markings for other shapes can be easily interposed.

Fluting Jig. The construction of a simple fluting jig is shown in Figs. 8 and 9, page 46. The dividing head is drilled with a suitable number of holes, and is fastened to the arbor by means of a pin inserted through the head and engaging the arbor. The dead center is simply a bolt turned to a 60° point. Adjustments to suit various lengths of work can be made by means of the slotted base arrangement, as shown in

Fig. 3 shows tenoning of round stock.

Ornamental radial rosettes in many patterns can be made with the simple jig shown in Figs. 4 and 5.

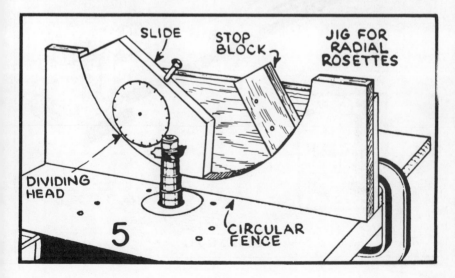

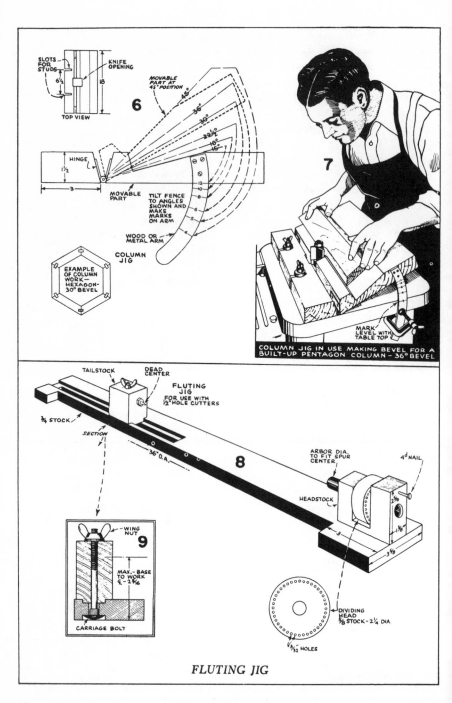

SLOTS FOR STUDS

6½

18

KNIFE OPENING

TOP VIEW

6

MOVABLE PART AT 45° POSITION

45°

36°

30°

22½°

18°

16°

HINGE

1½

3

MOVABLE PART

TILT FENCE TO ANGLES SHOWN AND MAKE MARKS ON ARM

WOOD OR METAL ARM

COLUMN JIG

EXAMPLE OF COLUMN WORK— HEXAGON— 30° BEVEL

7

MARK LEVEL WITH TABLE TOP

COLUMN JIG IN USE MAKING BEVEL FOR A BUILT-UP PENTAGON COLUMN — 36° BEVEL

TAILSTOCK

DEAD CENTER

FLUTING JIG FOR USE WITH ½" HOLE CUTTERS

¾ STOCK

SECTION

36" O.A.

8

ARBOR DIA. TO FIT SPUR CENTER

4ᵈ NAIL

HEADSTOCK

2¾

1⅜

3

3⅝

WING NUT

9

MAX.— BASE TO WORK ₵ — 2⁹⁄₁₆

CARRIAGE BOLT

DIVIDING HEAD ⅝ STOCK — 2¼ DIA.

¹⁄₃₂" HOLES

FLUTING JIG

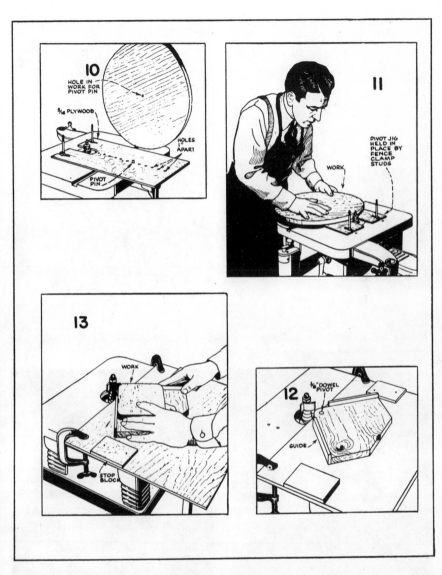

Fig. 9. This jig is for use with ½″ hole cutters. The distance from the lower side of the base to the centerline of the work must not exceed 2⁵⁄₁₆″—this being the highest position which it is possible to raise the cutter. A smaller jig for use with ⁵⁄₁₆″ hole cutters can be made up if desired. Larger work of any nature will require the use of a special extension spindle.

Pivot Jig. Round and semi-circular work can be shaped easier and more uniformly if a pivot jig is used. A simple form of construction is shown in Fig.

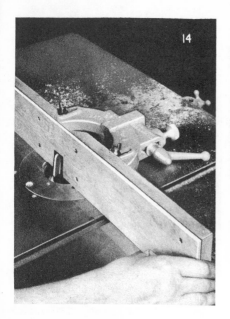
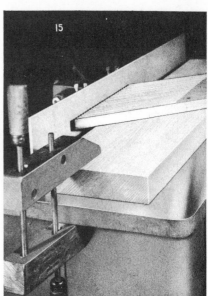

Figs. 14 and 15 show the auxiliary fence and clamp arrangement for panel raising on your cabinet shaper.

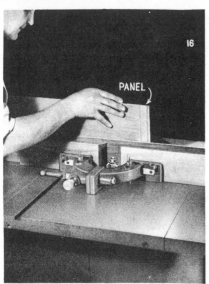
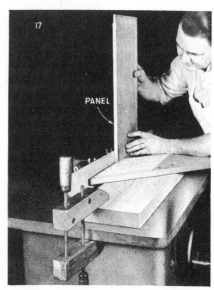

Figs. 16 and 17 show a panel being cut with the use of the jig and shaper cutter number D-214.

10, page 47. The jig consists of a piece of plywood, in which is drilled a series of holes 1" apart, these holes being about 5/16" diameter to take a corresponding pivot pin. Slots at one end of the jig permits of ready mounting to the shaper table, and also allows for proper setting where the work is not an even-inch diameter. The jig in use is shown in Fig. 11. A hole is drilled in the underside of the work to take the pivot pin. The cut is started by leaving the clamp studs loose so that the work can be pushed into the cutter to the required depth, after which the studs are tightened and work rotated into cutter with the pivot pin as a center. Work need only be rough sawed for this operation.

Rounding Corners. A handy jig for rounding corners is shown in Figs. 12 and 13, page 47. It consists of an auxiliary wood base, on which is mounted a pivoted carriage. In use, as shown in Fig. 13, the work is placed on the carriage and tight against the guides. The carriage is then swung from the starting stop lock to the finishing stop block to neatly and uniformly round the corner of the work.

Radial Rosettes. An unusual type of jig for making radial rosettes is shown in Figs. 4 and 5, page 45. The jig consists of a circular fence, on which is a sliding block. A dividing head is fitted into a round hole cut in the sliding block, the setting of the dividing head being controlled by a push pin in the block. In use, the work is fastened by brads or screws to the dividing head, and, at the various settings, pushed past the cutter. A stop block on the fence stops the cut at the required limit. The cutter is

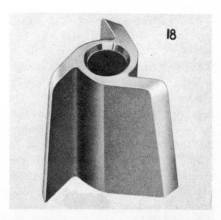

Fig. 18 pictures the D–214 shaper cutter used for panel raising.

usually of the same form as used for reeding and must be very sharp in order to prevent tearing the wood. Rosettes of this kind are useful in decorating furniture and can be made up to about 5" square. They make up best if the center is first recessed, this opening to be later fitted with a round, turned button projecting slightly above the face of the work. Fig. 4 shows a rosette with creases radiating from the center, but other forms radiating from the center of an edge or from a corner can be readily made by setting the fence accordingly. In doing production work of this nature, it is advisable to secure special cutters which are constructed and ground for this type of work. For the occasional job, standard cutters will work satisfactorily, but they must be very sharp and the feed must be made slowly to prevent tearing in those cuts which are directly across the grain. In any case, the jig should be well-constructed and well-guarded in order to eliminate any danger to the operator.

Panel Raising. Panel raising may be done on several different machines and with a variety of cutters. One of the easiest and most efficient methods is shown in Figs. 14 to 17, page 48. Shaper cutter number D-214, Fig. 18, page 49, was made specifically for this purpose. The first step after mounting the cutter on your shaper is to fasten a strip of ¼" plywood to the face of the shaper fence as shown in Fig. 14. With the fence studs loosened gradually feed the auxiliary fence into the cutter blade until it cuts through slightly more than the depth you wish to cut. Back the fence away from the cutter slightly and then tighten the studs. From a length of ⅝" or ¾" stock make a series of band saw cuts to a depth of four or five inches thus forming a series of flexible fingers which help to hold the panel against the fence while it is being cut. This is fastened to a wood block and clamped in place on the surface of the shaper table as shown in Fig. 15. The distance between the clamp and the fence should be great enough to allow movement of the panel through the gap with just enough pressure to hold it against the shaper cutter. The panel is then cut to its overall size and then run through the fixture as shown in Figs. 16 and 17.

CHAPTER NINE

Miscellaneous Shaper Operations

Jointing. Stock up to 1½" thick can be edge jointed on the shaper with perfect results. The fences are set much the same as the tables are set on a jointer (see page 21). The depth of cut is from zero to about 2", the deeper cuts requiring the fence to be mounted with the clamping studs in the rear set of holes. Extremely heavy cuts, as shown in Fig. 3, page 52, are not recommended for the average run of work, but the operation is sometimes useful, as, for example, in forming the handles of wooden paddles.

Tapering. Similar to the same operation as performed on the jointer, the front fence is set back the distance of the required taper, and, from a starting position as shown in Figs. 1 and 2,

the work is pushed forward to make the cut. Tapering on the shaper has two advantages: (1) A greater depth of cut is possible than on the jointer; (2) A fence extension for long work is easily attached to the standard fence. Where the work is to be both tapered and moulded, the whole operation can be done in one pass by using the required shaped knife instead of a straight cutter.

Shaping Figures. Very frequently shaped figures are necessary for games

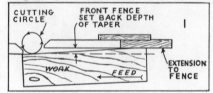

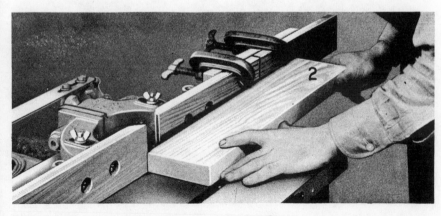

Taper jointing on the shaper is shown in Figs. 1 and 2.

and toys. Again, the job might entail the making of several hundred alphabets of wooden letters. This class of work is often done by comparatively slow scroll saw methods, whereas a much quicker solution is to work the mould in long strips on the shaper and then saw off the design to the required thickness. Several runs may be neces-

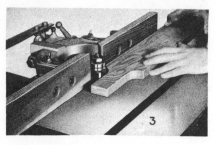

Making a heavy cut is shown in Fig. 3.

sary to produce the required figure, and special cutters ground to the required outline are sometimes worthwhile in order to speed up the cutting operation by reducing the number of passes required.

Turnings. This is another example of production work on the shaper, especially useful in getting out porch column bases, wall rosettes for stair rails, and also smaller pieces such as drawer knobs, small turned pediments, etc. Large work is usually shaped with a round pattern; smaller work is best swung from a pivot or worked in a jig (see page 47). A typical pattern set-up is shown in Figs. 6 and 7, page 54. The pattern is used above the work, and has handles to permit easy and safe

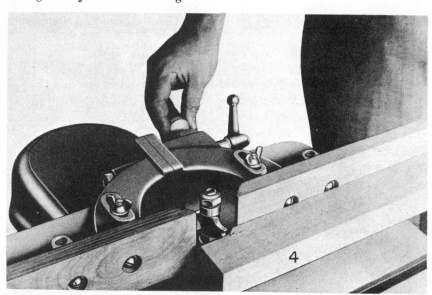

Fig. 4. Both halves of the shaper fence are adjustable through one control. With the one knob as shown above one-half of the fence may be moved either in front of or behind the surface of the other half. The handle to the right of the operator's hand locks the fence in position after it is adjusted.

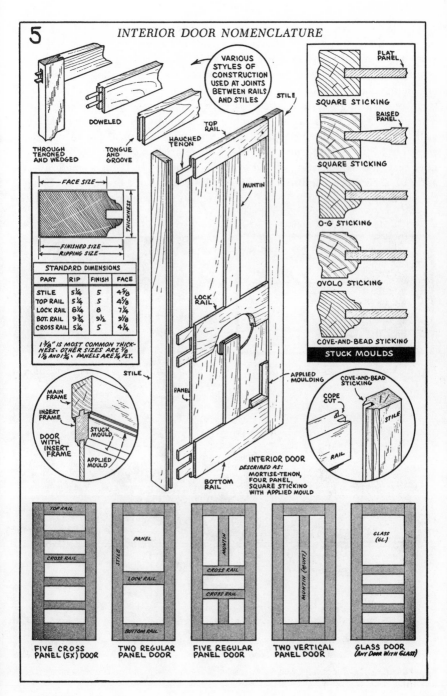

5 INTERIOR DOOR NOMENCLATURE

VARIOUS STYLES OF CONSTRUCTION USED AT JOINTS BETWEEN RAILS AND STILES

DOWELED

THROUGH TENONED AND WEDGED

TONGUE AND GROOVE

TOP RAIL

HAUNCHED TENON

STILE

MUNTIN

LOCK RAIL

FLAT PANEL

SQUARE STICKING

RAISED PANEL

SQUARE STICKING

O-G STICKING

OVOLO STICKING

COVE-AND-BEAD STICKING

STUCK MOULDS

STANDARD DIMENSIONS

PART	RIP	FINISH	FACE
STILE	5¼	5	4⅝
TOP RAIL	5¼	5	4⅝
LOCK RAIL	8¼	8	7¼
BOT. RAIL	9¾	9½	9⅛
CROSS RAIL	5¼	5	4¼

FACE SIZE

THICKNESS

FINISHED SIZE

RIPPING SIZE

1⅜" IS MOST COMMON THICKNESS. OTHER SIZES ARE ⅞, 1⅛ AND 1¾. PANELS ARE ¼ PLY.

STILE

MAIN FRAME

INSERT FRAME

DOOR WITH INSERT FRAME

STUCK MOULD

APPLIED MOULD

PANEL

APPLIED MOULDING

COVE-AND-BEAD STICKING

COPE CUT

STILE

RAIL

BOTTOM RAIL

INTERIOR DOOR
DESCRIBED AS:
MORTISE-TENON, FOUR PANEL, SQUARE STICKING WITH APPLIED MOULD

TOP RAIL

CROSS RAIL

FIVE CROSS PANEL (5X) DOOR

STILE

PANEL

LOCK RAIL

BOTTOM RAIL

TWO REGULAR PANEL DOOR

MUNTIN

CROSS RAIL

CROSS RAIL

FIVE REGULAR PANEL DOOR

MUNTIN (MUNT)

TWO VERTICAL PANEL DOOR

GLASS (GL.)

GLASS DOOR
(ANY DOOR WITH GLASS)

manipulation. Regular cutters can often be used, while some classes of work will demand knives ground to the required contour. Where heavy cuts are being made, a starting block instead of a starting pin should be used. The block is cut to the same contour as the knife and mounted close to it, as shown in Fig. 6. In this position, it permits easy and safe starting of the cut and also serves as a chipbreaker while the cut is in progress.

Panel Raising. Raised panels are featured in both casework and furniture construction, the essential feature of the work comprising a heavy panel which is reduced in thickness at all edges to fit a corresponding groove in the frame for which it is intended. Fig. 8 pictures a typical job in operation. There are two general methods of raising panels: (1) Using a small saw and tilting the work to suit, (2) Using a regular two-wing panel cutter, with the

Fig. 6 shows a formed starting block.

Using a pattern for a turning operation is shown in Fig. 7.

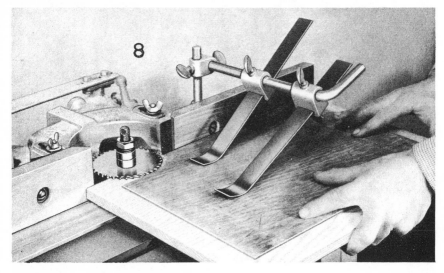

Panel raising using a small saw blade.

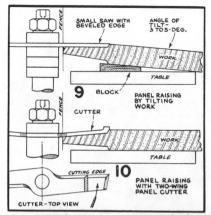

Figs. 9 and 10 show two methods of panel raising.

work flat on the table. The set-up for the first method of operation is shown in Fig. 9. A small saw with the teeth slightly beveled, is mounted on the shaper spindle. A strip of wood is then fitted to the shaper table or nailed to the shaper fence, this block, together with the edge of the shaper table, forming an angle of from 3 to 5 degrees. The work rides the block and the edge of the shaper table to get the angle required, while the edge rides the fence to keep the cut straight. The cut may or may not be made in one pass de-

pending upon how much wood is to be removed. Generally speaking, one or two fairly heavy roughing cuts followed by a light finishing cut will give better work at a speed comparable with a one-cut operation with its consequent slow feed. Heavy cutting in any kind of work is to be avoided unless special equipment is used.

The set-up for raising panels with a two-wing panel cutter is shown in Fig. 10. Here, the required tilt is incorporated in the construction of the knife so that the work is carried flat on the shaper table.

Making Dowels. Perfect dowels,

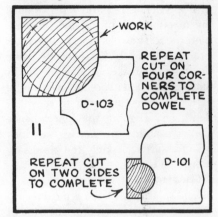

Fig. 12. Perfect dowels in a wide variety of sizes can be made on the shaper with standard cutters.

especially the larger sizes, can be made by using various cutters on the shaper. The largest size which can be made with standard knives is 1⅛″ diameter, this being done with D-231 cutter in the manner shown in Fig. 12, page 55. Four cuts are necessary, one on each corner, to reduce the square stock to cylindrical form. The finished work is a full round, smooth, and superior to ordinary hand turning. Other sizes which can be made with the four-cut method comprise ¼″, ⅜″, ½″, ⅝″, ¾″ and 1″, the larger sizes being the most practical. Smaller dowels are best made with the second method shown in Fig. 11. This requires but two cuts, one on either side of the stock, to complete the full dowel shape. D-102 cutter produces a dowel ¼″ in diameter, while D-101 cutter makes a dowel ⅜″ in diameter. Either method demands a little care in setting the cutter to the right depth and aligning the fence, hence the advisability of making a stock quantity after making the necessary adjustments.

Sanding. The shaper makes an excellent spindle sander, a typical operation being shown in Fig. 13. Fig. 14 shows one method of adapting a standard spindle and sanding drum, the spindle being cut off to fit the hole in the sanding drum. Other methods of mounting drums can be readily figured out by the operator to fit existing equipment. Fig. 15 shows a wooden disk for sanding panels. This type of sanding equipment is readily carried on the shaper spindle. One fault of the shaper as a spindle sander is that the machine, except for the smallest spindles, runs at excessive speed. This high speed tends

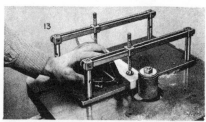

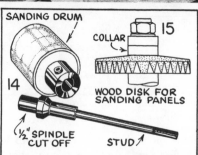

Sanding operations demand slow speed— a satisfactory manner of drive being from the drill press as shown in Fig. 16.

to glaze the sandpaper, resulting in burned work which is generally unsatisfactory. The obvious solution is to reduce the spindle speed to about 2000 r.p.m. This can be easily done by removing the front belt guard to permit access to the spindle pulley. Any motor can then be belted direct, a simple set-up being shown in Fig. 16 which utilizes the drill press for this purpose. The slow-speed set-up is useful for a number of varied operations, and is sometimes necessary to free the shaper

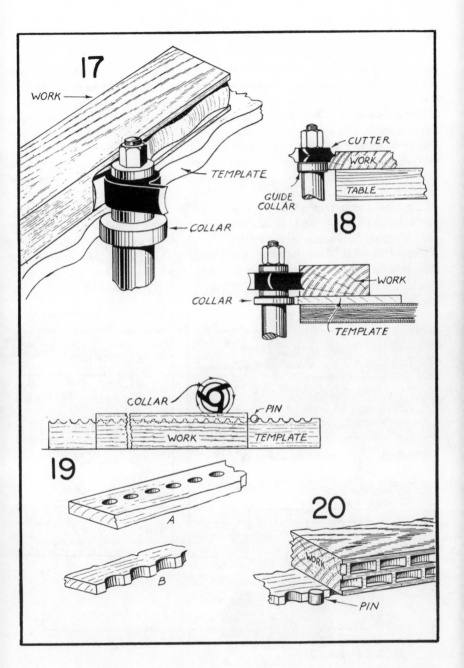

Ornamental mouldings are easily made on the shaper with $\frac{5}{16}$ in. hole cutters by using the simple methods shown in Figs. 17–20.

spindle after long disuse in extremely cold weather. Grinding with 3 or 4″ cup or straight wheels can be done at the low speed, while smaller wheels can utilize the full shaper speed.

Ornamental Work. Small shaper cutters are especially suitable for making fancy mouldings and a wide variety of forms can be cut with a minimum of setting-up. A typical example is shown in Figs. 17 and 18, page 57.

Another method capable of wide variation is shown in Figs. 19 and 20. The template in this case has a regular series of notches along its edge, the simplest way to form these being to

drill a row of holes as at A, Fig. 19, and then saw through them as at B. A short pin, a trifle less in height above the table than the thickness of the template, is set in the starting-pin hole in the table, and the cutter and two depth collars of the same diameter are placed on the spindle. The collar diameter limits the cuts to the proper depth, which should not be over ³⁄₁₆″ in most cases, making use of the small cutters. The work is then bradded to the template, parallel to the notched edge, one notch is set against the pin and the work is swung carefully into the cutter and against the collar. As soon as it

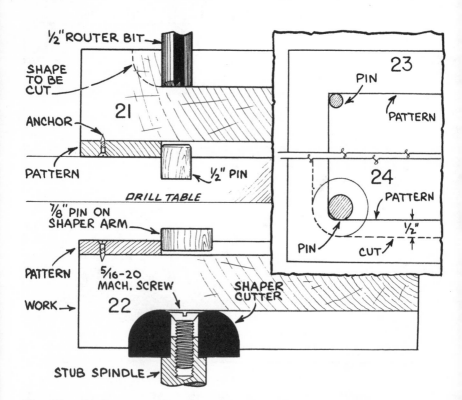

Figs. 21 to 24 show operations in machining round bottom recesses.

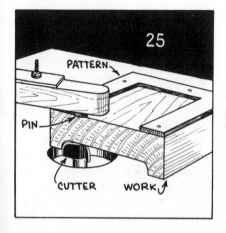

Round-bottom recesses are cleanly cut by using a special cutter mounted on the shaper stub spindle as shown in Figs. 25 and 26.

touches the collar it is swung back, the template is advanced to another notch and the process is repeated. This is continued for the entire length of the piece. The spindle may then be raised higher, the work moved forward on the template a distance equal to half a space and a second row of cuts made.

Routing. With a special chuck made to fit the main shaper spindle, all routing operations can be done on the shaper. Where pattern work is being done, the guide pin is located on the arm of the ring guard. All operations are similar to routing as done on the drill press except that the router bit points up instead of down. This is a useful method for doing pierced work since the pattern is always visible.

Round-Bottom Recesses. Wooden trays and pipe racks are typical projects which usually require the machining of a recess with rounded edges at the bottom. In the case of small rounds, the job can be done quite nicely with a ½″ round-nose router bit, running the work on either the drill press or shaper as desired. Larger rounds are cut on the

shaper, using a special cutter. The cutter is made from a ¾″ wide straight shaper cutter. This is chucked in the lathe, as in Fig. 27, page 60, and the entire center area relieved slightly with the use of a small hand grinder while the lathe is revolving. The grinder is then mounted on the lathe slide rest, the compound being set at 41 degrees. At this angle, a bevel about ¹⁄₁₆″ wide is ground on the spindle hole of the cutter, as shown in Fig. 28. This bevel is to house the head of a ⁵⁄₁₆″ flat head machine bolt, which can be seen in the picture. By means of the screw, the cutter is mounted on a shaper stub spindle and the spindle chucked in the lathe. With the lathe revolving, the cutter can be ground to shape by holding the grinding wheel against it. After the shape has been secured (a round of ½″ radius is recommended), the cutting edges are ground for back clearance on the bench grinder.

The operation of cutting the recess follows standard practice, using a guide pin and a plywood pattern. A roughing cut should be made with a

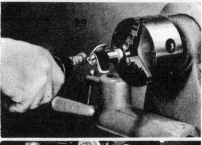

½″ router bit, as shown in Figs. 21, 23, page 58, and Fig. 30, page 60, this operation being done on the drill press. The guide pin should be ½″ diameter and the pattern should be ½″ less than the required shape. The work is then run on the shaper, using the special cutter and a guide pin ⅞″ in diameter, the pin being mounted on a wooden arm bolted to the ring guard bracket, as can be seen in Fig. 26. Fig. 24, page 58, shows that with a ⅞″ guide pin, a 1⅞″ diameter cutter will cut ½″ beyond the pattern, hence the need of making the pattern ½″ undersize.

The depth setting of the shaper cutter is best obtained by placing the work over the cutter and then elevating the spindle until the cutter lifts the work a hair off the table. In addition to cutting the round, the cutter will also make a very clean end cut if properly ground and can be used to clean up the machine marks made by the router bit.

Rip Planing. When the shaper is fitted with a rip fence of the type commonly used on the circular saw, many operations in planing, grooving, etc. can be done. The operation differs from the usual job of running an edge against the regular shaper fence in that the work is planed to exact width, whereas the ordinary shaper operation simply smooths the edge. In common with all cuts of this type where the work is supported on the side opposite the cutting action, there is a tendency of the cutter to "hog" the work, that is, pull the work into the cutter. This is shown by the arrows in Fig. 33. The dotted lines show the position of a hold-in, which should always be used for this type of work.

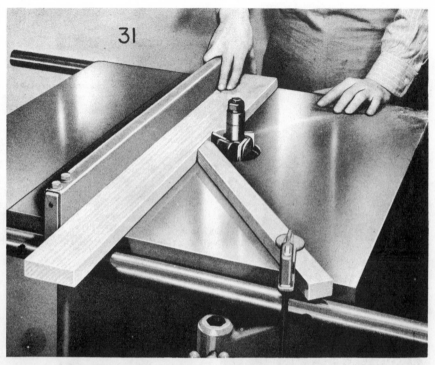

Rip-planing on the shaper dresses rough boards to exact width.

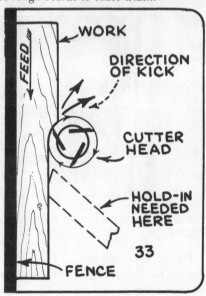

FEED

WORK

DIRECTION
OF KICK

CUTTER
HEAD

HOLD-IN
NEEDED
HERE

33

FENCE

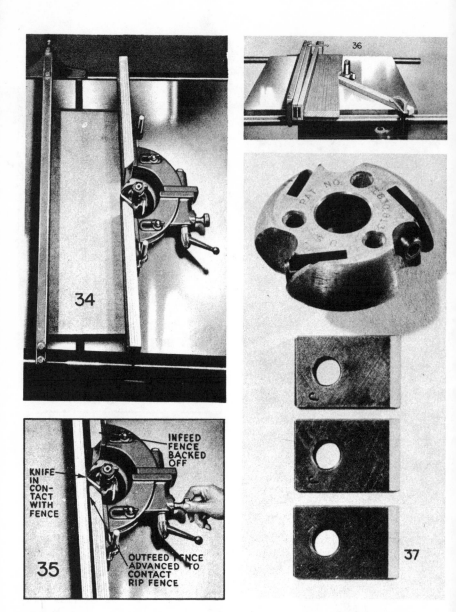

Figs. 34 to 36. Some type of hold-in must always be used in rip planing to prevent hogging.

Fig. 31 shows the set-up. There is no limit to the depth of cut, although it is poor practice to plane over ½″ unless for some special reason. The ring guard should be used. The complete set-up is shown in Fig. 32. If a large three-knife cutterhead, Fig. 37, is being used, the guard should be about ⅛″ above the head. On all other heads and knives, the guard is placed in contact with the work, providing a hold-down as well as a guard.

The regular shaper fence can be used as a hold-in if desired, as shown in Fig. 34, page 62. Only the outfeed fence is used, the infeed fence being backed off. The manner of setting the shaper fence or any other type of hold-in is shown in Fig. 35. The rip fence is first advanced into contact with the knife. The infeed fence (shaper) is backed off to full limit. The outfeed fence is advanced until it contacts the rip fence, at which setting it will be aligned with the work as it leaves the cutterhead. The rip fence is then set to the desired width of work and the cut made. Check should be made to see that the hold-in is in close contact with the work since any play between the work and the hold-in would defeat its purpose.

Fig. 36 shows the use of the rip fence in connection with a tapering jig. The method of working is just the same as before, with the exception that the work is held and advanced by the jig.

CHAPTER TEN

Grinding Shaper Cutters

Rake Angle. The rake angle of any cutter determines its shape and other characteristics. As shown in Fig. 1, a slanting line across a piece of wood is necessarily longer than a straight one. Applied to shaper cutters, it can be seen, Fig. 2, that the length of the cutter working on an angle, B, must be greater than if the cutter worked straight across the work, as at A. This rake angle is present in all shaper cutters and is greatest when knives are mounted in a moulding head, as shown in Fig. 3, where the angle is approximately 30 degrees. It is obvious that the greater the rake angle, the greater the difference between the shape of the knife and the moulding it cuts.

Amount of Bevel. Knives are beveled at an angle between 30 and 45-degrees. It can be seen, Fig. 6, that a bevel which will provide clearance at the outer cutting circle may not be enough to provide clearance at the inner cutting circle. Examination of a factory-sharpened cutter will show that the bevel is greatest at the inner edges of the knife, thus maintaining the same exact amount of clearance. Portions of the knife parallel with the line of travel, such as the sides, demand only a minimum amount of bevel to provide clearance.

Projected Shape. The required shape of any cutter to produce a cer-

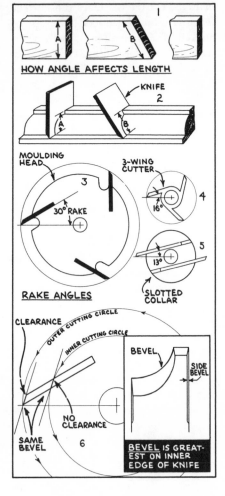

Figs. 1–6 show factors governing the knife shape.

64

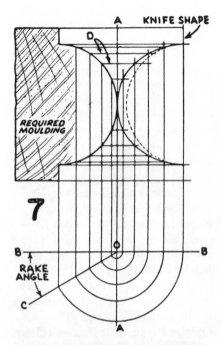

Fig. 7 shows knife projection diagram.

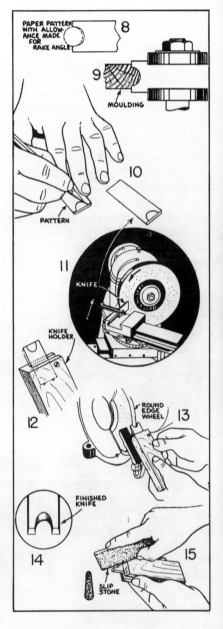

Figs. 8–15 show knife making.

tain shape can be obtained by drawing the moulding full size on a piece of paper, as shown in Fig. 7. Along the edge of the moulding erect a vertical line, A. Below the moulding, draw a horizontal line, B and where A intersects B draw a line, C, at the same angle as the rake angle of the cutter. Drop lines from the moulding shape to the line C, and, using O as a center, carry these lines around to line B on the opposite side and then project them upwards. Lines D located at all points where the vertical lines cut the moulding are then carried across the center line and establish a series of marks, which, when they are joined, show the shape of the cutter required to cut the moulding. The difference is slight, amounting to about $\frac{1}{16}''$ in depth where moulding head cutters are being plotted and about half of this for three-wing cutters and slotted collars. For average work, the projected shape can be judged with fair accuracy without drawing. The basic rules to remember are (1) knives for cutting beads must be ground deeper, and (2) knives for cutting coves must be ground fuller.

Making a Knife. Figs. 8 to 15, page 65, show the various steps in making a pair of knives for use with slotted collars. The required shape is a full half-circle, as is shown in Fig. 9. A paper or metal pattern is then made, as shown in Fig. 8, and, following the same basic rule, this is cut slightly deeper than the shape of a true circle. Fig. 10 next shows the pattern shape being transferred to the knife blanks. The outer straight bevel is then ground, a suitable method being as shown in Fig. 11 which uses the lathe slide rest to set the required angle. The curved portion of the knife is then ground on a round edge wheel, as shown in Fig. 13, the tool rest being adjusted to provide the proper bevel. After grinding both knives, the shape is compared and checked, readjustments made as required, after which the bevel is lightly honed, as in Fig. 15, to remove any burr left by the grinding. On certain shapes, good use can be made of a cut-off wheel to remove excess knife stock, thereby eliminating tedious grinding.

Use of Shaped Wheels. Wheels can be fashioned to any required shape by using a suitable dresser. The revolving wheel type is the fastest cutting, but does not permit the precision which is possible with the silicon carbide stick type or the diamond dresser. The wheel type should be pushed straight into the wheel, while the stick or diamond work best at a drag angle,

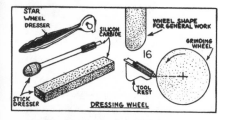

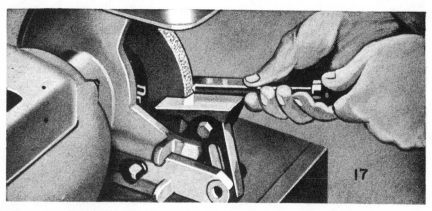

Fig. 17. A diamond point dresser is the best tool for precision shaping of wheels preparatory to knife grinding.

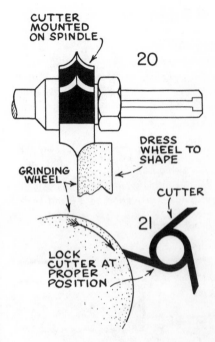

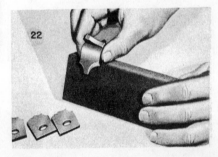

as can be seen in Fig. 16. With a wheel properly shaped, it is a simple matter to grind any cutter to the same contour. Fig. 18 shows a three-wing cutter being ground. Stops and guides insures all wings being ground exactly the same. The use of a shaped wheel in a tool post grinder used on the lathe is shown in Figs. 19, 20 and 21. The cutter is turned to the required position for the bevel, as in Fig. 21, and is then locked in this position by means of the index pin, after which the cut can be made.

Sharpening Knives. Factory-ground shaper knives with involute bevels should be sharpened by honing the flat side of the cutting edge, as shown in Fig. 22. The involute bevel will retain the same shape regardless of metal removed from the back side. Knives ground in the homeshop with a straight bevel can be resharpened in the same way, or, the bevel itself can be honed. Where the knife has an in-

Grinding blank knives for the shaper cutter head is easily and accurately accomplished with the lathe and the compound tool rest. Figs. 23 and 24 show the method of holding and grinding a blank knife to obtain a straight bevel edge for planing or rabbeting.

Fig. 25 shows one method of holding blank knives for grinding a cove or curved edge. The edge of the grinding wheel is first shaped with a diamond wheel dresser to the correct curve desired on the knife edge. The knife is then clamped onto the compound tool rest with the aid of the cutter bar holder. The work is slowly fed into the grinding wheel by means of the feed handle, using oil to prevent burning.

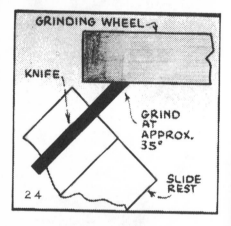

volute or curved bevel, however, no grinding or honing should be done on the bevel.

Grinding Blank Knives. The lathe is an excellent medium for grinding and shaping blank knives for your shaper. The compound tool rest offers an excellent and accurate method of holding and advancing the cutter blades into the grinding wheel which is mounted on the head stock of the lathe. By marking and maintaining accurate

Fig. 26. A clean well ground edge on the shaper cutter blades is a necessity in order to obtain a flawless professional look to the mouldings which you intend to run on your shaper. Always feed the work by advancing it into the cutter slowly and steadily. Do not crowd or overload the spindle or poor work will be the result.

settings with the compound tool rest exact duplicates of intricate shapes are easily obtained by using this equipment. This takes the guess work out of making a matched pair of shaped knives. Accurate clearance angles for the cutting edges are also easily maintained. Always use a cutting oil when grinding blank knives and feed slowly into the grinding wheel so that you do not remove the temper from the high speed steel.

CHAPTER ELEVEN

Application of Shaper Cutters

Square Stuck Doors. Use the shaper set-up shown in Fig. 4 to groove the inside edge of all pieces. Cope both ends of both rails with the set-up shown in Fig. 5. Assemble the door as shown in Fig. 1. For light cabinet doors, the tongue-and-groove formed by sticking makes a sufficiently stiff joint when well glued. For sturdier construction, the joints can be doweled, Fig. 2, or tenoned, Fig. 3.

Bead-and-Ogee Sticking. Figs. 7 and 8 show the assembly of a cabinet door, bead-and-ogee stuck on one side. The operations are the same as before, using the set-up shown in Fig. 9 for the sticking, and the set-up in Fig. 10 to cope the ends of the rails. Figs. 11 and 12 show the assembly of a door stuck on both sides. This sticking is standard for 1⅛" closet doors. The joints are doweled.

Applied Mouldings. Doors are frequently made up with applied mouldings. Fig. 15 shows a flush mould. The main frame is square stuck, after which the panels and moulded strips are fitted in place. A somewhat similar form of construction is shown in Fig. 16. This is good for very heavy doors, the main frame being square stuck with tenoned joints, while the insert frame is stuck for ¼" panels.

Windows. Figs. 17 to 20, page 72, show the construction of the upper

sash of a double-hung, check-rail window. The top rail and stiles are 2" wide, face measure, which is a fair standard, while the check rail is 1¾" wide by 1¼" thick. The first step in construction involves a careful layout of the wood stock. The size of the window must be determined, the basic dimensions being the glass size or the size of the opening into which the window must fit. All mortises and tenons should be carefully marked. Wood to be removed should be penciled with a heavy "x." The name of each piece should be plainly written on the best side of the wood, this side to be known thereafter as the face side. Since wood stock will often vary a little in thickness, it is important to keep the face side in the same position for all pieces.

The first machine operation after jointing and trimming the stock consists of cutting the mortises, as shown in Fig. 25, page 74. The rails are then taken to the circular saw and the shoulder cuts for the tenons are made, as in Fig. 26. Some form of stop should be used in order to keep the dimension uniform. The tenon cheek cuts are then made, using the two saws with a spacing collar, as shown in Fig. 27, page 75, or one saw and making cuts on either side. The top rail and stiles are next conveyed to the shaper where

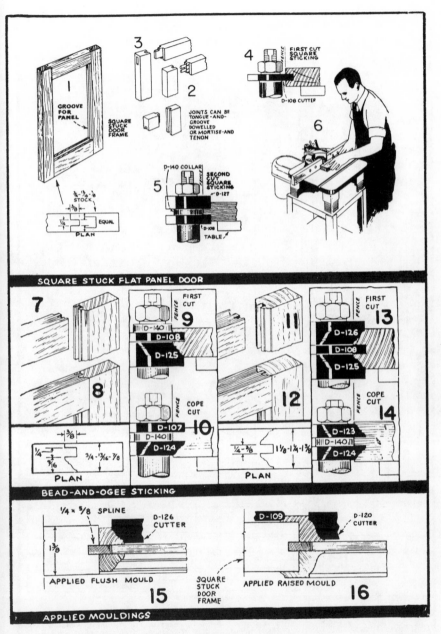

Figs. 1–16 show application of shaper cutters in cabinet and interior door construction. All doors use ¼ in. flat panels, although raised panels with the same edge thickness could be substituted if desired.

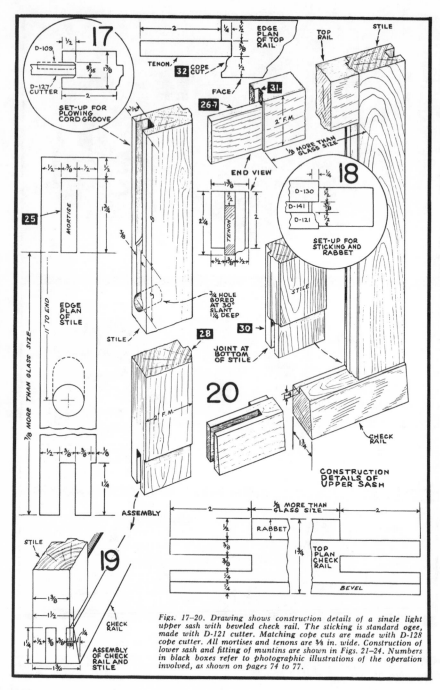

Figs. 17–20. Drawing shows construction details of a single light upper sash with beveled check rail. The sticking is standard ogee, made with D-121 cutter. Matching cope cuts are made with D-128 cope cutter. All mortises and tenons are 3/8 in. wide. Construction of lower sash and fitting of muntins are shown in Figs. 21–24. Numbers in black boxes refer to photographic illustrations of the operation involved, as shown on pages 74 to 77.

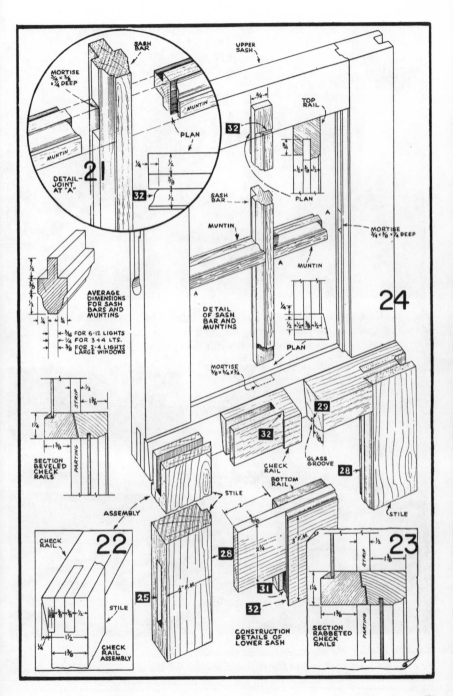

SASH BAR

UPPER SASH

MORTISE
¾" × ⅜"
× ¼ DEEP

MUNTIN

PLAN

21

MUNTIN

DETAIL—
JOINT
AT "A"

32

¼

½

⅜

½

AVERAGE
DIMENSIONS
FOR SASH
BARS AND
MUNTINS

¼   ¼

— ³⁄₁₆ FOR 6-12 LIGHTS
— ¼ FOR 3+4 LTS.
— ⅜ FOR 2-4 LIGHTS
    LARGE WINDOWS

¾

32

TOP
RAIL

³⁄₈

½   ⅜   ½

PLAN

SASH
BAR

MUNTIN

A

A

A

MUNTIN

MORTISE
¾" × ⅜" × ¼ DEEP

24

¼

½

½   ⅜   ½

DETAIL
OF SASH
BAR AND
MUNTINS

PLAN

MORTISE
⅜ × ¾ × ¾

29

GLASS
GROOVE

STRIP

½

1⅜

1¼

1⅜

PARTING

SECTION
BEVELED
CHECK
RAILS

32

CHECK
RAIL

28

STILE

ASSEMBLY

CHECK
RAIL

22

STILE

2" F.M.

25

1¼   ⅜   ⅜   ½
⅛
¼

1½

1⅜

CHECK
RAIL
ASSEMBLY

STILE

BOTTOM
RAIL

2

⁵⁄₈

2¼

3" F.M.

28

31

32

CONSTRUCTION
DETAILS OF
LOWER SASH

STRIP

½

1⅜

1¼

23

1⅜

PARTING

SECTION
RABBETED
CHECK
RAILS

Fig. 25. Cutting the mortises in one of the stiles. The wood area to be removed should be carefully marked, centering the cut ½ in. from each edge of the 1⅜ in. stock. The face side of the wood should be towards the operator.

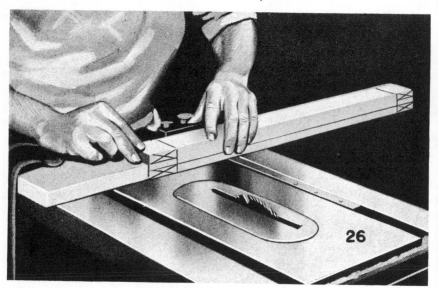

Fig. 26. Making the shoulder cuts on the ends of the top rail. Notice the stop block to accurately set each cut to the required length. Set the saw blade shallow, cleaning out the corner of the shoulder with the cheek cut shown in Fig. 27.

Fig. 27. *A double saw with ⅜ in. spacing collar is used to make the tenon cheek cuts. The cut should be carefully centered, and the thickness of the tenon checked for a snug fit in a ⅜ in. mortise. A single saw can be used if desired.*

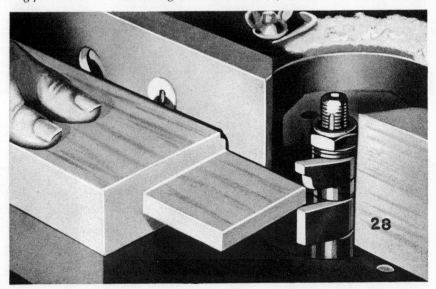

Fig. 28. *Sticking the edges of the stiles and rails, using D-121 cutter. The rabbet is cut at the same time. The fence should be set to cut a rabbet ¼ in. deep. The ogee cutter will then take a corresponding bite. Use D-141 collar.*

Fig. 29. Sticking the bottom edge of the lower sash check rail. The glass groove is cut at the same time or can be made in a separate operation (see text). The appearance of the cut when finished is as shown in the foreground.

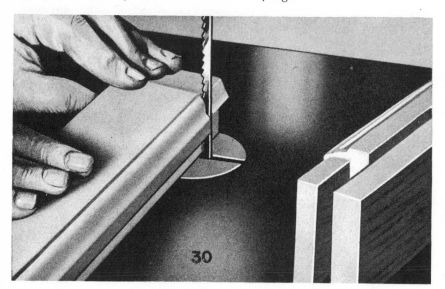

Fig. 30. Trimming the ogee mould at the bottom of the upper sash stiles to permit a neat joint with the check rail. The operation is done on the band saw. Piece in foreground shows finished appearance.

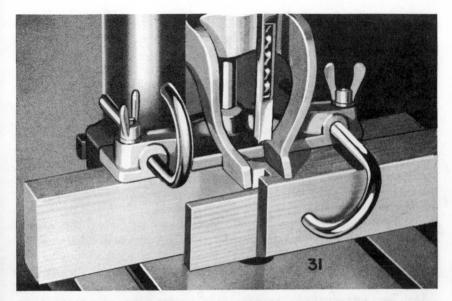

Fig. 31. Mortising the upper rail so that it will fit the corresponding shoulder on the stile. The cut should be in line with the tenon, and should extend in ¼ in. The same operation is necessary on the underside of the bottom rail.

Fig. 32. Cope cutting the rails, using D-128 cutter. The wood is held in the shaper sliding jig, the depth of the cut being controlled by the stop rod. This cut should be checked carefully for proper height and depth setting.

they are stuck with the set-up shown, Fig. 28. The check rail is not stuck, but is rabbeted only. The sticking on the lower end of the stiles for the length of the tenon is now cut away on the band saw, as in Fig. 30, page 76. The next operation, Fig. 31, page 77, consists of mortising the top rail in line with the tenon and in ¼". Finally, the top rail is coped at both ends, Fig. 32, after which the assembly of the sash can be made. After checking the joints, the check rail is removed for beveling. The plowed groove for the cord is not run in until the sash is permanently fitted together. Similar operations in the construction of the lower sash are, of course, done at the same time as the upper sash.

Sash Bars and Muntins. Very frequently, the sash, especially the upper one, is divided into a number of smaller lights. Vertical uprights which separate the panes of glass are called *sash bars,* while the shorter horizontal strips are called *muntins.* All of the light wood inside a sash is often referred to as muntins or munts. The manner of fitting sash bars and muntins is shown in Fig. 21, page 73. The necessary marking and cutting of the mortises in the main frame would be made at the same time as other previous operations. The muntins are 1⅜" thick to match the thickness of the sash, but vary somewhat in width, being narrower where the sash has many lights. Approximate average dimensions are given in the drawing and will be found suitable for most work. The stock for all of the sash bars necessary should be in block form. In this shape, it is cut to exact length and coped at the end which is to fit the top rail. The end which fits to the check

rail is square-cut to the tenon dimensions shown. After this cutting to length, the wood stock is ripped into pieces of the required width. Each piece is then stuck on both sides with the same set-up as used for the main frame.

Muntins are made in the same manner as sash bars, with the exception that the tenons are flush with the ends, as can be seen in the circle inset, Fig. 21, page 73. Mortises to receive the munts are thus the same depth as the glass rabbet, or ¼". The joint between muntin and sash bar is the same as muntin to stile. The wood stock should be cope-cut in block form before being ripped to width for sticking. This will insure uniform length.

Construction of Lower Sash. With a few minor variations, the construction of the lower sash is the same as the upper sash, as shown at the bottom of Fig. 24. The bottom rail is fitted exactly the same as the top rail. The check rail shows two variations. One of these concerns the joint between the rail and stile, the rail being cope-cut to match the sticking on the stile. Variation number two is that the under edge of the rail is stuck, and is not left square as for the upper sash. A glass groove substitutes for the glass rabbet as shown in Fig. 4, page 71.

Building Trim. Figs. 33, 34 and 35 show various mouldings used in building trim.

Storm Sash. The stock used is generally 1⅛" thick. Typical window frame construction can be used. A simpler style with square sticking is shown in Figs. 36 to 43, page 80. The main feature of the construction is the tenon with long and short shoulders cut with

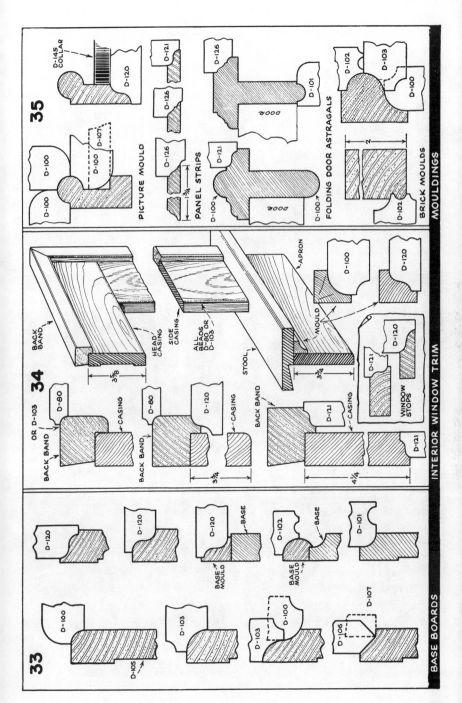

35

PICTURE MOULD

PANEL STRIPS

FOLDING DOOR ASTRAGALS

BRICK MOULDS

34

INTERIOR WINDOW TRIM

33

BASE BOARDS

MOULDINGS

79

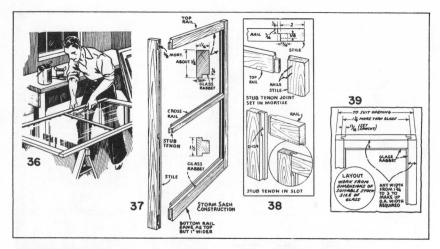

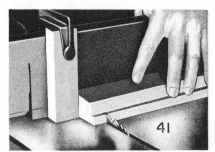

Fig. 40. The glass rabbet can be cut in a number of different ways. As good a method as any is the "two pass" cut with a single saw blade, as shown.

Fig. 41. To secure the required ¼ inch offset, the shoulder on the long side of the tenon is cut on the circular saw, $1\frac{3}{16}$ inch from the end and level with rabbet.

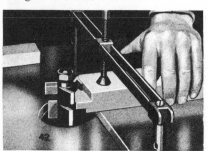

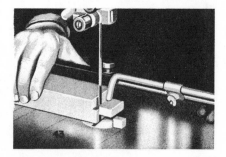

Fig. 42. The two stock sizes of Delta straight shaper cutters combine with the saw cut to produce the ¼ inch offset tenon.

Fig. 43. The haunch on top and bottom rails can be easily cut on the band saw, using the stop rod as a guide.

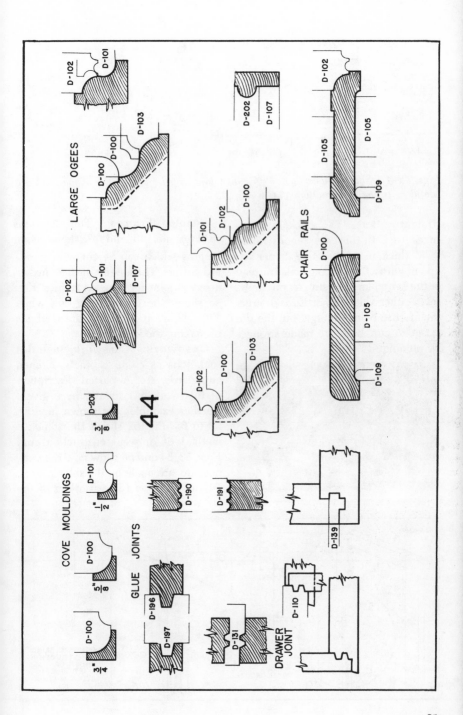

LARGE OGEES

D-102 D-101
D-100 D-100 D-103
D-102 D-101 D-107
D-101 D-102 D-100
D-102 D-100 D-103

D-202 D-107

CHAIR RAILS

D-102
D-105 D-105
D-105 D-109
D-100
D-105
D-102 D-100 D-109

COVE MOULDINGS

D-101 1/2"
D-100 5/8"
D-100 3/4"
D-201 3/8"

44

GLUE JOINTS

D-190
D-191
D-196 D-197
D-131

DRAWER JOINT

D-139
D-110

81

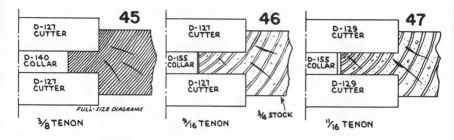

Figs. 45–47. Short tenons up to $1\frac{1}{16}$ inch long can be cut on the shaper and are useful in frame construction.

straight cutters. $1\frac{3}{16}''$ stock is sometimes used. In this case, tenons would be ¼'' thick, using the same shaper set-up but with a ¼x¾ spacing collar instead of the ⅜x¾ collar. The stub tenon can be set in either a slot or mortise as desired, the mortise being stronger but the slot easier to cut. Both are made stronger by pinning.

Paneled Frames. The diagrams in Figs. 45, 46 and 47 show tenon lengths which can be cut with standard cutters. The longest of these makes an ideal joint for paneled frames. Fig. 48 shows the tenon being cut, while Figs. 49, 50 and 51 illustrate methods of making the joint.

Casework. Casework includes such jobs as china cabinets, kitchen cupboards, etc. A partial description of this work has already been given. Further examples are shown in Figs. 52 to 63. Fig. 52 shows the standard method of drawer construction, and Figs. 53, 54 and 55 show how the various cuts are made on the shaper. Figs. 56 and 57 show two variations of the

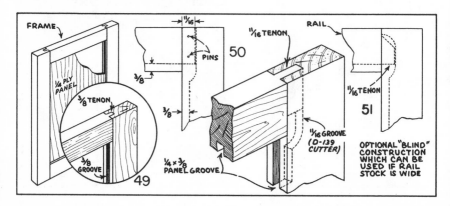

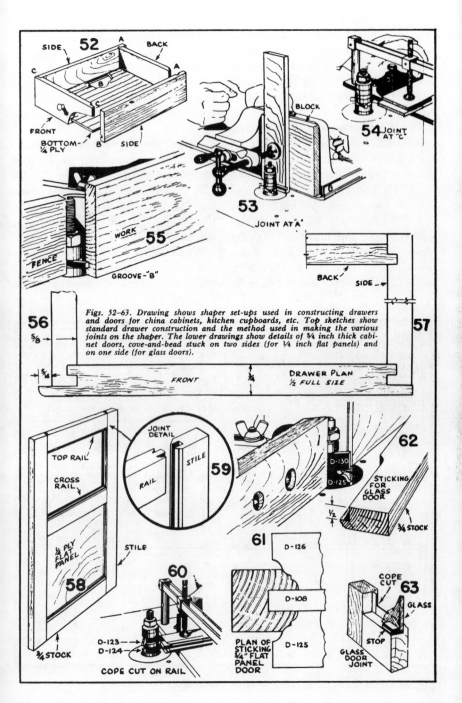

52 SIDE A BACK A C

FRONT BOTTOM—¼ PLY B SIDE

54 JOINT AT "C"

53 JOINT AT "A" BLOCK

55 WORK FENCE GROOVE—"B"

BACK SIDE **57**

56 ⅝ 5/16 FRONT ¾ DRAWER PLAN ½ FULL SIZE

Figs. 52–63. Drawing shows shaper set-ups used in constructing drawers and doors for china cabinets, kitchen cupboards, etc. Top sketches show standard drawer construction and the method used in making the various joints on the shaper. The lower drawings show details of ¾ inch thick cabinet doors, cove-and-bead stuck on two sides (for ¼ inch flat panels) and on one side (for glass doors).

58 TOP RAIL CROSS RAIL ½ PLY FLAT PANEL STILE ¾ STOCK

JOINT DETAIL RAIL STILE **59**

62 D-130 D-125 STICKING FOR GLASS DOOR ½ ¾ STOCK

61 D-126 D-108 D-125 PLAN OF STICKING ¾" FLAT PANEL DOOR

60 D-123 D-124 COPE CUT ON RAIL

63 COPE CUT GLASS STOP GLASS DOOR JOINT

83

joint between the drawer front and the sides. The projecting lip style is usually cut with a dado head on the circular saw since the depth of cut is somewhat deeper than is possible with standard cutters.

The construction of a ¾" thick cabinet door, cove-and-bead stuck on both sides, is shown in Fig. 58, page 83. The shaper set-up for the sticking is shown in Fig. 61. The rails are cope cut in the usual manner, the set-up being as shown in Fig. 60. Panels are ¼" plywood. The joint is simply glue-fastened (Fig. 59) although dowels can be used if additional stiffness is desired. Where matching glass doors are to be made,

the stiles and rails are stuck with the set-up shown in Fig. 62. The cope cut in this case would simply be one of the cutters shown in Fig. 60, instead of two. Fig. 63 shows the assembly of the glass door, using a wood stop to hold the glass.

Miscellaneous Mouldings. Several miscellaneous mouldings made with ½" hole cutters are shown in Fig. 64. The crown mouldings are fashioned from flat stock, the bevels being cut on the circular saw after the shaping is finished.

Wood Joints. Fig. 65 pictures various edge-to-edge and corner joints which can be cut on the shaper. The

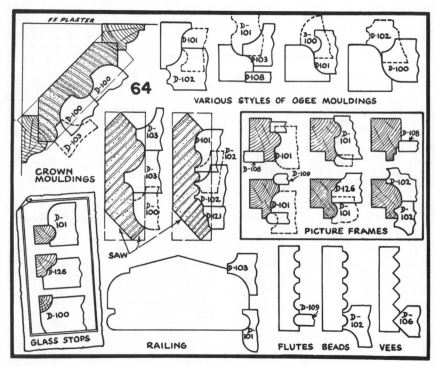

Fig. 64 shows drawings of miscellaneous mouldings.

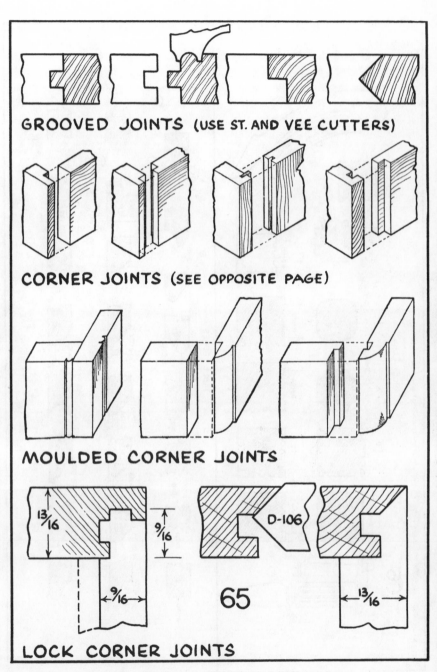

GROOVED JOINTS (USE ST. AND VEE CUTTERS)

CORNER JOINTS (SEE OPPOSITE PAGE)

MOULDED CORNER JOINTS

13/16   9/16   D-106   13/16
9/16

65

LOCK CORNER JOINTS

Fig. 65 shows various edge and corner joints.

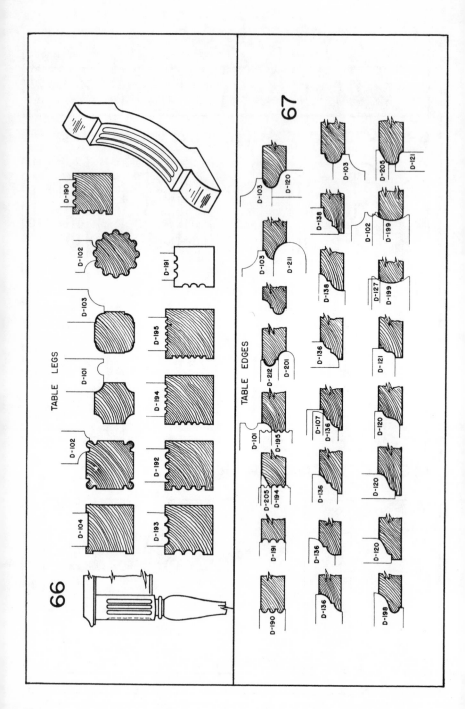

TABLE LEGS

D-190
D-102
D-103
D-101
D-102
D-104
D-191
D-195
D-194
D-192
D-193
66

TABLE EDGES
67

D-103 D-120
D-103 D-211
D-101
D-212 D-201
D-205 D-194
D-191
D-190

D-103
D-138
D-138
D-136
D-107 D-136
D-136
D-136

D-205 D-121
D-102 D-199
D-127 D-199
D-121
D-120
D-120
D-198

D-195

drawing is self-explanatory, and the cutters required should be obvious.

Table Tops. Shaped edges suitable for table tops are shown in Fig. 67, page 86. These shapes can often be used to advantage as strip mouldings or in some other capacity. Similarly, many of the moulded edges shown in the building trim drawings can be adapted for furniture work. For this reason it is advisable to study all of the shapes in this chapter, even though you may not be interested in the particular classification under which the shapes are listed as shown in some of the examples. Three or four cutters of the same pattern are often useful, especially for reeding or fluting flat work. With but the one cutter in the standard set, jobs of this nature must be reset for each new cut, whereas with three or four cutters mounted together on the spindle, the whole operation can be done in one pass of the work, an important saving in time, especially on production work.

Small Cutters. Small cutters with $\frac{5}{16}''$ spindle hole are useful for a wide

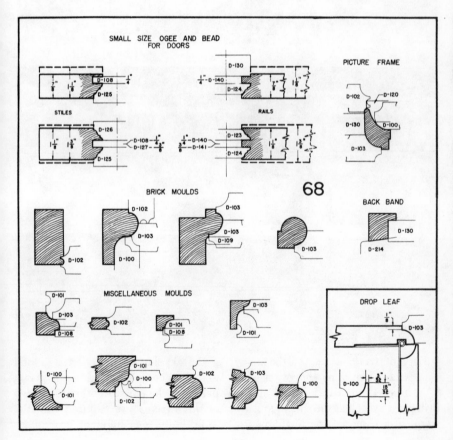

variety of work, a few of the many shapes possible being shown on page 97. These cutters can be used on the drill press as well as the shaper and are frequently essential for small shapes.

Certain shaper cutters are designed to make a complete moulding with one pass over the knife. At other times two or three passes are required with the same knife in a different position or

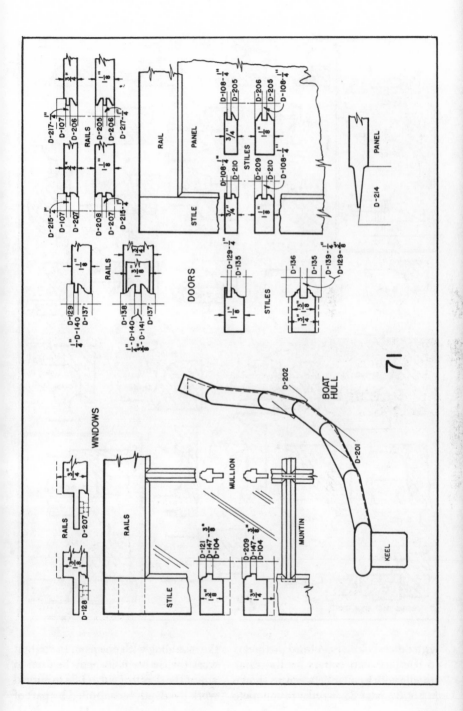

71

89

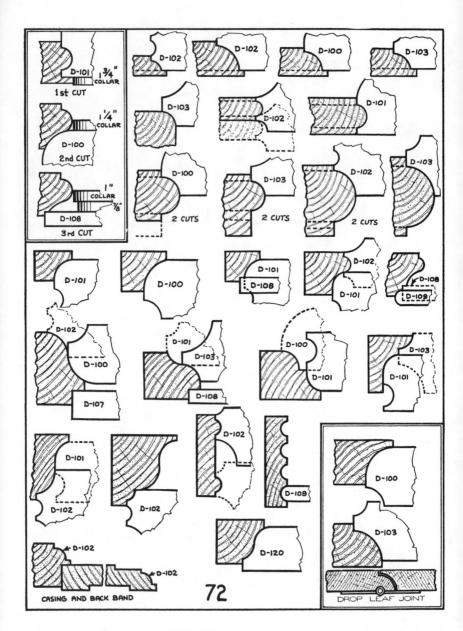

with different knives. A third method is to combine two cutters on the same spindle with a collar between, as shown in Fig. 69, page 88, in order to complete the moulding with one pass. In straight work the shaper fence may be used to adjust the depth of cut, while in curved work the depth is controlled by part of

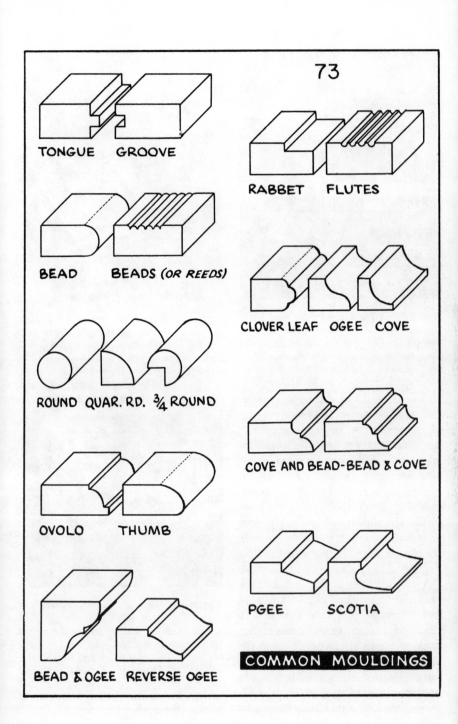

73

TONGUE GROOVE

RABBET FLUTES

BEAD BEADS (OR REEDS)

CLOVER LEAF OGEE COVE

ROUND QUAR. RD. ¾ ROUND

COVE AND BEAD-BEAD & COVE

OVOLO THUMB

PGEE SCOTIA

BEAD & OGEE REVERSE OGEE

COMMON MOULDINGS

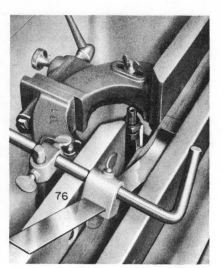

Figs. 74 and 75. The circular saw fence acts as a guide for jointing the edge of straight lumber with the use of either the three lip straight cutter or the moulding head with straight knives.

Long narrow stock is jointed on one edge by using a three lip straight cutter and passing the strip through the opening left between the regular shaper fence and the circular saw fence. The work is held firmly down on the shaper table with the spring hold-down clip shown in Fig. 76.

the uncut moulding riding on a collar. The wood facing on the fence may be shifted toward or away from the cutters. This makes it possible to reduce the opening in the fence to a minimum thus increasing the safety and adding further support for small lengths of moulding. The fence opening has been reduced as shown in Fig. 70, page 88, since both the cutter and the spindle are smaller than the ones pictured in Fig. 69.

A wide selection of shaper knives are available to produce almost any contour or shape you may desire in a moulding. In many cases, however, two or three passes are required using the same cutter or a combination of two or three standard shapes to produce a completed moulding. Fig. 72, page 90, shows a variety of moulding shapes to-

The shaper fence is adjusted as shown in Fig. 77 so that after the jointed edge passes over the shaper cutter the newly formed width will fit snug but not tight between the shaper fence and the circular saw fence. The near or lead-in fence of the shaper should be moved back so that ample clearance is left for the unjointed edge of the stock.

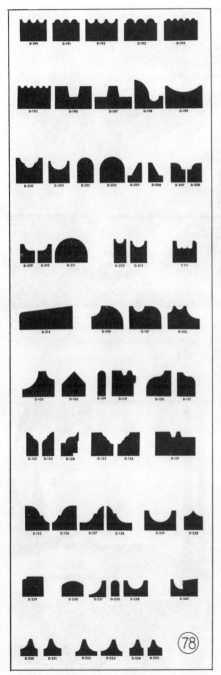

You have here now a complete line of 3-lip shaper cutters by which thousands of different shapes and mouldings can be made efficiently and accurately. They have a ½" hold and can be used on not only Delta-Industrial shapers, but any shaper that has a ½" spindle. These Delta 3-lip shaper cutters are made of special alloy steel that is especially tough and keeps a sharp cutting edge. They are hardened and tempered in oil, as are all good tools, so that they will not only stand up under severe service, but can also be resharpened without losing their cutting quality. They are resharpened merely by grinding across the face of the cutting edge on a straight, flat grinding wheel, or a cup wheel, if one is available.

gether with the cutters or combination of cutters necessary to complete the mouldings. Many of the mouldings are shown in the various stages of their successive cuts. Some of these mouldings can be adapted for furniture work such as table edges, shelf front and side frame mouldings, while others will work out well for casing and corner mouldings.

Jointing. The standard shaper fence, being fully adjustable, permits the machine to be used as a jointer when desirable. To joint with the shaper, use a wide, straight knife, set with rear half of the fence (left-hand) exactly level with the top of the knives —just as the rear table of the jointer is set. Adjust the front half of the fence for the depth of cut and proceed to joint the work. This feature of the fence is also very desirable when moulding work where all the face must be cut away; in such cases the rear half of the fence is simply adjusted to support the work as it leaves the cutter.

The versatility of the shaper as pictured in Fig. 79 shows a simple method of using a sanding drum, shaper collars, and a contour form complete with indexing head to give the final sanding finish to an octagonal turned table leg.

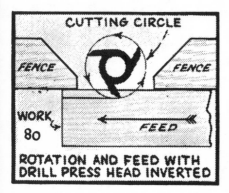

The drill press will make an emergency shaper producing good results provided that the cutting is not too heavy. The drill press head may be used for shaping operations either in the regular or inverted positions as shown in Figs. 80–83.

94

The fence is normally mounted so the wood-face is parallel to the miter gage slot. However, holes are provided in the table so the fence can be mounted at right angles to this position, in case the extra table extension leaf is used.

The utility of the shaper is increased considerably because of the fact that many accessories are available for special types of work. An additional aid in shaping is made available by mounting the fence and guide bars from your circular saw on the cabinet as shown in Figs. 74 and 75. The circular saw fence will act both as a guide and a positive width adjustment on wide stock.

The Drill Press. May be used as a shaper in two ways—either "right side up" or inverted. Fig. 81 shows the drill press in operation as a shaper in the inverted position. Since the work must always be fed against the rotation of the cutter, it is apparent that the cutter must be placed on the spindle so that the lips face to the right, the work being fed from right to left as diagrammed in Fig. 80. When the drill press is used in the regular position, the cutter lips face to the left and the feed is from left to right, as shown in Figs. 82 and 83. Of the two positions, the regular position is by far the most practical for the occasional shaper job because of the simplicity of changing over from drill press to shaper. The inverted position has some slight advantages, but they are more than outweighed by the trouble of reversing

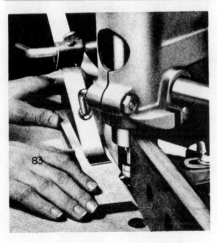

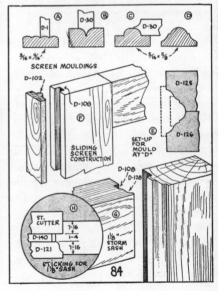

Fig. 85. *Collars play an important part in shaping operations.*

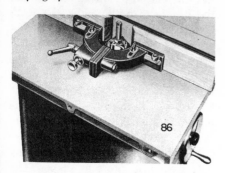

Fig. 86. *Your cabinet shaper may be used for large high production work. The table is 27 by 28 inches with a ⅜″ by ¾″ groove for miter gauge jigs. The table may be increased to 27 by 36 inches by adding a rear extension table.*

the head every time the machine must be converted into a shaper. For home-craft work, the regular position is more satisfactory.

Cutters and collars have standard ⁵⁄₁₆″ diameter holes to fit the ⁵⁄₁₆″ threaded shank of a special spindle. Instead of a special separate spindle most operators use an adapter spindle which fits the regular routing spindle. The adapter should never be used in the regular drill chuck, as this brings the cutters too far below the bearings in the drill press quill. Even with the special spindles, the extension or over-hang, should be kept as small as is consistent with the work to be done.

Screen and Storm Sash. There are a great many methods used in screen and storm sash construction. Some typical examples of construction and the moulding cutters required for the necessary shaper work are shown in Fig. 84, page 95. The storm sash as shown in G is constructed of 1⅛″ material. The moulding required for this frame may be cut in two passes on your shaper using the two cutters required or it may be cut in one pass as shown in Fig. 69, page 88. Various screen mouldings are shown in Figs. A, B, C, and D.

Combination Spindle Cuts. Many of the more delicate and intricate mouldings are made by combining cuts made with both the ⁵⁄₁₆ and ½″ spindles. None of these shapes have been shown in this chapter, but it can be easily seen that the number of mouldings which could be cut by thus combining the small and large cutters is limited only by the imagination of the craftsman.

Fig. 87. *Interchangeable spindles allow you to use a wide variety of cutters on your shaper.*

88

97

CHAPTER TWELVE

Cove-and-Bead Shaper Cutters

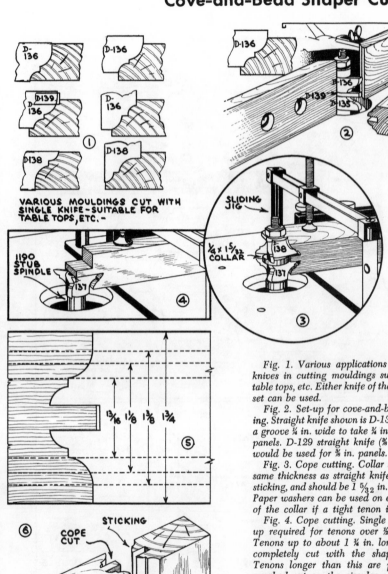

VARIOUS MOULDINGS CUT WITH
SINGLE KNIFE—SUITABLE FOR
TABLE TOPS, ETC.—

Fig. 1. Various applications of single knives in cutting mouldings suitable for table tops, etc. Either knife of the matched set can be used.

Fig. 2. Set-up for cove-and-bead sticking. Straight knife shown is D-139, cutting a groove ¼ in. wide to take ¼ in. plywood panels. D-129 straight knife (⅜ in. wide) would be used for ⅜ in. panels.

Fig. 3. Cope cutting. Collar should be same thickness as straight knife used for sticking, and should be 1 ⁵⁄₃₂ in. diameter. Paper washers can be used on either side of the collar if a tight tenon is desired.

Fig. 4. Cope cutting. Single knife set-up required for tenons over ½ in. long. Tenons up to about 1 ¼ in. long can be completely cut with the shaper knife. Tenons longer than this are preferably roughed cut on the circular saw before coping.

Fig. 5. Plan of cove-and-bead sticking as applied to various thicknesses of wood.

Fig. 6. Sketch showing cove-and-bead sticking applied to 1 ⅜ in. stock (standard for interior and exterior doors).

99

Application of 3-Knife Cutterhead

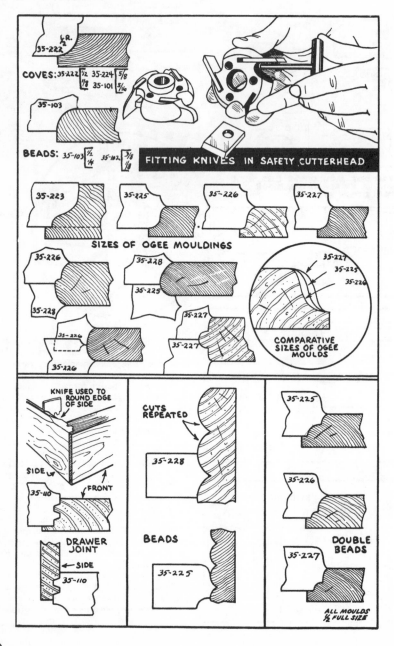

FITTING KNIVES IN SAFETY CUTTERHEAD

SIZES OF OGEE MOULDINGS

COMPARATIVE SIZES OF OGEE MOULDS

DRAWER JOINT

BEADS

DOUBLE BEADS

ALL MOULDS ½ FULL SIZE

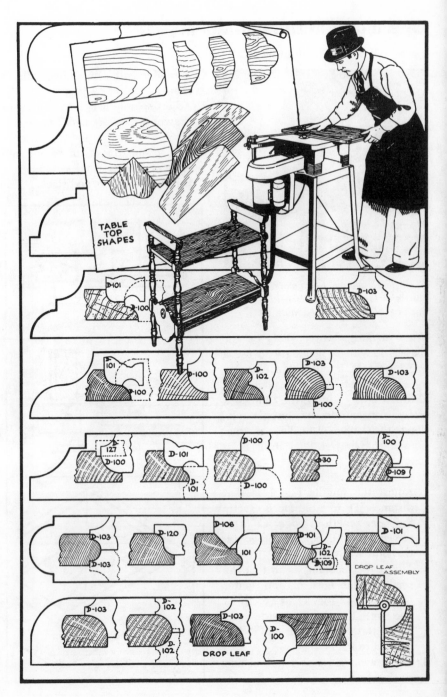

TABLE TOP SHAPES

D-101
D-100
D-103

101
D-100
D-102
D-103
D-100
D-103

127
D-100
D-101
D-100
D-101
D-100
D-30
D-100
D-109

D-103
D-103
D-120
D-106
101
D-101
D-102
D-109
D-101

DROP LEAF ASSEMBLY

D-103
D-102
D-102
D-103
D-100

DROP LEAF

Operations in Drawer Making

WITH THE D-110 SHAPER CUTTER

This photo shows how work is gaged from the table top and is held with the backing block in the tenoning jig.

When making drawer joints on the shaper, it will be necessary to use a backing block fitted to the tenoning jig as shown at "X" in the photo and also in Fig. 1 to bring the thin stock of the drawer sides into proper relation to the shaper cutter. The construction of the drawer joint itself is as follows:

1. Adjust the spindle Fig. 1 so that distance "D" to table top is exactly the same length as edge "C." This is very, very important, otherwise the joint will not fit.
2. Adjust the tenoning jig so that the smallest diameter of the cutter (Edge "C" in Fig. 1), is exactly in line with the drawer inside face. The cutter must not cut into it, just tangent to it.
3. Cut drawer sides as required and stack.

4. Assemble cutter on stub spindle in shaper.
5. Adjust spindle height so that lip of drawer just passes over top of cutter.
6. Adjust stop for depth of cut into ends of drawer front.
7. Cut drawer fronts and stack.

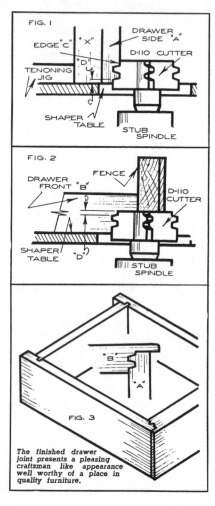

The finished drawer joint presents a pleasing craftsman like appearance well worthy of a place in quality furniture.

Making Glue Joints on the Shaper

WITH THE D-131 CUTTER

With this dual purpose cutter, perfect glue joints can be made with a single cutting tool which is so designed that the tongue and groove fit perfectly by merely reversing the stock for the mating cut. It replaces the two solid steel glue joint cutters commonly used in sash and door factories in which one cutter cuts the groove and another cuts the tongue. It has an additional advantage in that the design being reversible, produces extra holding surface for the glue as a result of the large matched sections. It makes a very practical method of building up small rather narrow boards into wide serviceable stock. Even when the end grain is exposed, the glue joint is neat and in no way objectionable. It is a comparatively simple job to make perfect glue joints on the shaper if these easy steps are followed:

1. Dress both pieces of stock on the jointer for a tight joint.
2. Set shaper fence halves even and move fence back so that smallest diameter of cutter is exactly in line with face of fence as shown at edge "C" Fig. 1.
3. Prepare piece of scrap material the exact thickness of the stock to be jointed and make a trial cut just far enough to get the full depth of cut, Fig. 2.

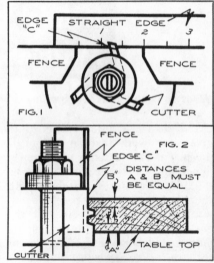

D-131

4. Check trial cut shoulders "A" and "B." Adjust height of spindle until both shoulders are exactly the same.
5. Cut one side of stock face side up, Fig. 3, and mating piece face down, Fig. 4, to complete the glue joint.

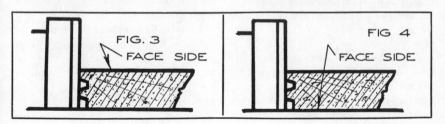

CHAPTER THIRTEEN

Helpful Hints About Machines and Accessories

What to Look For When You Buy a Shaper

The shaper is a tool designed to give your work that "professional" touch. For that reason it is extremely important that the shaper you buy be a sturdy, high-quality machine with simplified controls and precision adjustment features that take all the guesswork out of delicate shaping jobs. Listed below are a number of features to look for when you buy a shaper for your own use.

Established Manufacturer. It will cost less in the long run to buy your shaper from a manufacturer who has established through the years a reputation for top quality in the production of power tools for the industrial and home workshop markets. You can then be certain that your shaper will have the built-in accuracy features that make your woodworking jobs easy, and the long life, free from breakdowns, that makes your investment worthwhile.

Availability of Replacement Parts. Another plus feature in buying from an established manufacturer is the fact that you will always be able to get replacement parts no matter how old your shaper might be.

Availability of Accessories. Before you buy, check to make sure that the manufacturer of your shaper also produces a complete range of shaper cutters, spindles and other accessories,

designed for your machine. Thus you will be assured that the accessories you buy will fit your machine without the need for makeshift arrangements.

Sturdy, Easily Adjusted Fence. The fence on the shaper you buy should be heavy, simple and substantial, easy to adjust and a solid, safe unit when locked into position. Both halves of the fence should be independently adjustable to give greater accuracy and to save time in setting up the machine.

Short, Rigid Spindle. The spindle, which is the heart of the machine, should be short and sturdy, precision ground of heat-treated alloy steel so that the spindle "whip" which destroys the bearings is eliminated. Thus you will be assured of continuing accuracy in your work.

Sealed-For-Life Spindle Bearings. The spindle bearings should be closely set, sealed-for-life ball bearings to insure long service from the shaper you buy. Bearings should also be pre-loaded to prevent distortion at high speeds.

Simple, Convenient Controls. All controls should be convenient to the operator from the normal working position, yet safely removed from the moving parts of the machine. The control which locks the spindle at the derived height should be separate from the other adjustment controls and designed to avoid distortion of the ball bearing housings.

Compact Shaper Mechanism. The entire shaper mechanism, spindle, bearings and housing should be a complete, compact unit bolted securely to the table so that there is no possibility of disrupting the spindle alignment.

Interchangeable Cutter Spindles. The shaper should be so designed that cutter spindles are easily inter-changed, thus enabling you to utilize the various sizes of shaper cutters. The machine should also be adaptable to a stub spindle used in cope cutting on sash, doors and general cabinet work.

Complete Safety Features. Exposed belts and pulleys should be covered, and a ring guard should be available to protect the operator when doing free-hand work without the fence. Available accessories should include a safety shaping jig for use when shaping short or narrow pieces.

Proper Accessories Enable You to Do More Jobs . . . And to Do Them Easier and Faster

The jig holds work securely with no danger of slippage. It has a miter gage head so that angled work can be shaped with perfect accuracy.

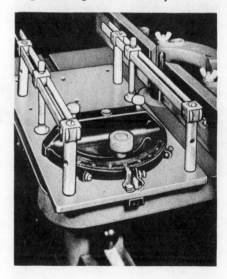

Sliding Shaper Jig. Shaping of short and narrow pieces is a safe and accurate operation when you use a sliding shaper jig.

Safety Cutterhead with Blank Knives. Self-hardening blank shaper knives are available to the craftsman who desires to make mouldings of his own design. The knives are sand blasted, so that the cutter design may be drawn directly on them and ground to shape.

All knives are ⅛″ thick with a 30° clamp angle. Available in ½″, ¾″, 1″ and 1¼″ widths; 2½″ long.

Safety cutterheads for use with the knives are available for either ½″ or ¾″ shaper spindles.

Spring Hold Down. Spring hold downs hold work firmly against the fence and table to permit accurate straight line shaping.

They can be used on either end of the shaper fence and will hold work up to 3½″ thick.

Safety Ring Guard. A safety ring guard is available to protect the craftsman when free hand shaping curved and irregular work.

It is fully adjustable and can be easily removed. When in use it also acts as an efficient hold down.

3-Knife Safety Cutterhead. A cutterhead is available which will allow you to use your circular saw moulding cutterhead knives on your shaper.

The head is made of alloy steel; fits either ½″ or ¾″ spindles. A useful accessory which gives you double usage out of the knives that you already own.

Shaper Cutters and Collars. Various sized collars and three-lip cutters with ⅝₁₆″ or ½″ holes are available in a wide variety of shapes that offer unlimited possibilities in making hundreds of different moulding designs.

These are one piece knives, with involute relief; honing the face does not change their shape. Knives can be combined to give complete, intricate mouldings in one pass through the shaper.

Shaper Spindles. A variety of easily interchanged spindles are available to permit the use of the complete range of cutters on your shaper. These include the ½″ stub spindle for cope cutters, the ½″ spindle for regular cutters with ½″ holes, and the ⁵⁄₁₆″ spindle for smaller cutters with ⁵⁄₁₆″ holes.

Tenoning Jig. A tenoning jig can be used to good advantage in various shaper operations, especially where narrow stock must be face shaped. This accessory makes close or awkward shaping work safe and easy.

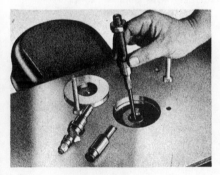

Steel Stand. A steel stand is available so that your bench shaper can be converted into a floor model machine. Sturdily constructed, it will bring your machine to the proper working height.

Reversing and On and Off Switch. A reversing and on and off switch is available for any standard split-phase or capacitor motor. This switch is ideal for the shaper where feed is needed in a counter clockwise as well as a clockwise direction.

Index